Beef up your Biology muscles with CGP!

Going for Grades 8-9 in Edexcel International GCSE Biology* is a heavyweight challenge...
you'll need to tone up your exam skills with plenty of practice on the difficult bits.

Luckily, CGP is here to help with a book full of questions as tough as any you'll
face in the real exams. They'll test your knowledge to the limit, topic by topic —
and there are two mixed practice sections to give your skills an exam-style workout.

Better still, we've included step-by-step answers at the back, so it's easy to mark your
work and find out which topics need most attention ahead of the real exams.

* This book also covers all the trickiest Biology topics from Edexcel's International GCSE Science Double Award.

CGP — still the best! ☺

Our sole aim here at CGP is to produce the highest quality books —
carefully written, immaculately presented and dangerously close to being funny.

Then we work our socks off to get them out to you
— at the cheapest possible prices.

Published by CGP

Editors:
Laura Collins, Camilla Sheridan, Hayley Thompson

Contributors:
David Martindill

With thanks to Philip Armstrong and Rachel Kordan for the proofreading.

With thanks to Ana Pungartnik for the copyright research.

ISBN: 978 1 78908 236 4

Clipart from Corel®
Illustrations by: Sandy Gardner Artist, email sandy@sandygardner.co.uk
Printed by Elanders Ltd, Newcastle upon Tyne.

Based on the classic CGP style created by Richard Parsons.

Contents

☑ Use the tick boxes to check off the topics you've completed.

Paper 2

The questions in this book test both Biology Paper 1 and Biology
Paper 2 material. Some material is needed for Paper 2 only — we've
marked Paper 2 questions in Sections 1-9 with brackets like this one.

If you're doing a Science (Double Award) qualification
you don't need to learn the Paper 2 material.

Exam Tips

Exam Basics

1) For the Edexcel International GCSE in Biology, you'll sit two exam papers at the end of your course. ⟶

2) If you're doing the Edexcel International GCSE in Science Double Award, you won't sit Paper 2.

3) Some material in the specification will only be tested in Paper 2. In Sections 1-9 of this book, the questions that cover Paper 2 material are marked with a Paper 2 bracket.

Paper	Time	No. of marks
1	2 hours	110
2	1 hr 15 mins	70

You Need to Understand the Command Words

Command words are the words in a question that tell you what to do.
If you don't know what they mean, you might not be able to answer the questions properly.

Describe This means you need to recall facts or write about what something is like.

Explain You have to give reasons for something or say why or how something happens.

Suggest You need to use your knowledge to work out the answer. It'll often be something you haven't been taught, but you should be able to use what you know to figure it out.

Calculate This means you'll have to use numbers from the question to work something out. You'll probably have to get your calculator out.

Here are a Few Handy Hints

1) **Always, always, always make sure you read the question properly.**
   This is a simple tip but it's really important. When you've got so much knowledge swimming round in your head it can be tempting to jump right in and start scribbling your answer down. But take time to make absolutely sure you're answering the question you've been asked.

2) **Take your time with unfamiliar contexts.**
   Examiners like to test you really understand what you've learnt by asking you to apply your knowledge in different ways. Some of these contexts can be quite tricky but don't let them trip you up — read all the information you're given really carefully and, if you don't understand it, read it again. You can make notes alongside the question or underline certain bits if it helps you to focus on the important information.

3) **Look at the number of marks a question is worth.**
   The number of marks gives you a pretty good clue as to how much to write. So if a question is worth four marks, make sure you write four decent points. And there's no point writing an essay for a question that's only worth one mark — it's just a waste of your time.

4) **Show each step in your calculations.**
   You might be a bit of a whizz at maths and be confident that your final answer to a question will be right, but everyone makes mistakes — especially when under the pressure of an exam. Always write things out in steps then, even if your final answer's wrong, you'll probably pick up some marks for your method.

5) **Pay attention to the time.**
   After all those hours of revision it would be a shame to miss out on marks because you didn't have time to even attempt some of the questions. If you find that you're really struggling with a question, just leave it and move on to the next one. You can always go back to it at the end if you've got enough time.

These handy hints might help you pick up as many marks as you can in the exams — but they're no use if you haven't learnt the stuff in the first place. So make sure you revise well and do as many practice questions as you can.

Cells and Transport

1   *Symbiodinium* is a plant-like protoctist. It contains colourful photosynthetic pigments, which give coral reefs their colour. Some bacteria can infect *Symbiodinium* cells and cause them to die. This can lead to the coral reefs losing their colour.

a)   Suggest **one** structural similarity and **one** structural difference between *Symbiodinium* cells and the bacteria that infect them.

Similarity: ....

Difference: ....

[2]

A group of scientists investigated how to kill a bacterial species that threatens *Symbiodinium* using a type of bacteriophage. Bacteriophages are viruses that infect specific bacteria. This often leads to the bacteria's death. The graph below shows some of the scientists' results.

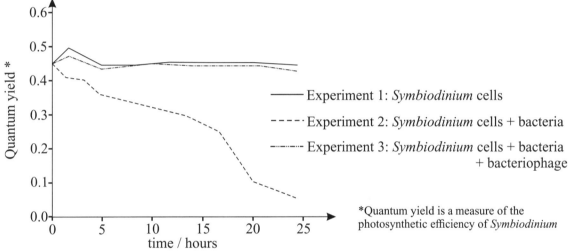

b)   i)   Explain why the scientists included Experiment **1** in their study.

....

....

....

[2]

ii)   Explain the difference between the results of Experiments **2** and **3**.

....

....

....

[2]

c)   Bacteriophages are viruses.
Give **one** reason why viruses are not considered to be living organisms.

....

[1]

[Total 7 marks]

2 Samples of plant and animal tissue were each placed into separate beakers containing a sugar solution. The table below shows the starting sugar concentrations of the cells and of the solutions in the beakers. Due to differences in their structures, the plant and animal cells responded differently to being placed in the solutions. Both sets of cells swelled up, but the animal cells burst and the plant cells did not.

	Sugar concentration inside cell (mol/dm^3)	Sugar concentration in beaker (mol/dm^3)
Plant	0.3	0.1
Animal	0.4	0.2

Suggest an explanation for the responses of both the plant and animal cells when placed in the sugar solutions.

....

....

....

....

[Total 3 marks]

3 Stem cells can be used in medicine to treat diseases. For example, diabetes is a condition that can be caused by the failure of beta cells in the pancreas to produce the protein insulin. Scientists think that it may be possible to treat diabetes by using stem cells to replace the faulty beta cells.

a) i) Name the process by which beta cells develop from stem cells in the embryo.

....

[1]

ii) Suggest **one** subcellular structure that there are likely to be many of in each beta cell.

....

[1]

b) Hematopoietic stem cells (HSCs) are found in the core of most adult human bones. Suggest why HSCs cannot be used to treat diabetes.

....

....

[1]

c) Research has shown that adult body cells can be changed into cells that have the same features as embryonic stem cells. Treating a patient with these cells would reduce the medical risk compared to using embryonic stem cells. Explain **one** other reason why using these modified adult body cells may be preferable to using embryonic stem cells.

....

....

....

[2]

[Total 5 marks]

Section 1 — The Nature and Variety of Living Organisms

4 All organisms need to exchange substances with their environment in order to survive. Single-celled organisms such as bacteria exchange substances with their environment directly across their outer surface. The rate at which they exchange substances is affected by their surface area to volume ratio.

A student carried out an experiment to investigate the relationship between the surface area to volume ratio of a bacterial cell and the rate of exchange of substances.

To represent bacterial cells, agar cubes were used. Agar is a material that absorbs substances from its surroundings. The agar contained an indicator dye and dilute sodium hydroxide solution (an alkali). The indicator dye is pink at a pH greater than 8, but becomes colourless when pH falls below 8. The diagram shows an agar block as well as some of the other equipment used in the experiment.

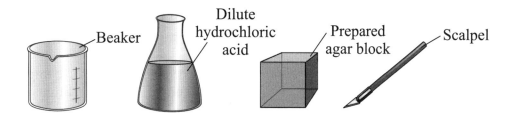

a) Describe a method that the student could have used in her experiment in order to obtain valid results.

....

....

....

....

....

....

....

....

....

....

....

....

[6]

b) Suggest **two** ways in which the agar in this experiment did not accurately represent a bacterial cell or how a bacterial cell exchanges substances with its environment.

1. ....

2. ....

[2]

Section 1 — The Nature and Variety of Living Organisms

The diagram shows two rod-shaped
bacterial cells, drawn to scale.

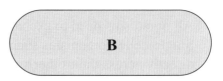

c) Both cells need to absorb substances from their environment in order to carry out metabolic
reactions. Based on this information and the diagram above, which cell (**A** or **B**) do you think
will have a faster metabolic rate? Explain your answer.

....

....

[2]

[Total 10 marks]

5   A scientist investigated the
diffusion of ammonia along a
glass tube. The apparatus she
used is shown in the diagram.

When the ammonia reaches the end of the tube, the litmus paper changes colour.
The scientist timed how long this colour change took at five different concentrations of ammonia.
Her results are shown in the table below.

Concentration of ammonia (number of drops)	1	2	3	4	5
Time (s)	79	68	121	63	54

a) The glass tube is 20.0 cm long.
Calculate the rate of diffusion for 1 drop of ammonia in mm per second.

.... mm per second
[2]

b) Identify the concentration of ammonia which produced an anomalous result.

.... drops
[1]

c) Ignoring the anomalous result, what conclusion can be made from this data about the effect of
ammonia concentration on the rate of diffusion?

....

[1]

d) Suggest **one** variable the scientist should have controlled in this experiment
and explain how she could have controlled it.

....

....

[2]

[Total 6 marks]

Exam Practice Tip

Questions that start with the word 'suggest' are some of the trickiest that appear in the
exams. 'Suggest' means you're not expected to have learnt the answer — instead, you're
supposed to use your scientific knowledge to work out what the answer might be.

Score:

31

Section 1 — The Nature and Variety of Living Organisms

Enzymes

1 Lipase is an enzyme that catalyses the breakdown of lipids. A student carried out an investigation into the effect of temperature on the rate of lipid digestion. When a lipid is digested by lipase, a pH change occurs due to the production of fatty acids. The student added lipase to a lipid sample and timed how long it took for this pH change to occur at a range of temperatures. The table shows his results.

Temperature (°C)	Time taken for pH change to occur (s)			
	1st trial	2nd trial	3rd trial	mean
10	292	299	291	294
20	256	257	261	258
30	240	235	239	238
40	217	224	219	220

a) i) Plot the mean time taken for the pH change to occur at each temperature on the grid. Draw a curve of best fit.

[4]

ii) Use your curve to predict how many seconds it would take for the pH change to occur at **35 °C**.

.... seconds

[1]

b) Suggest what is likely to happen if the student were to repeat the experiment at **60 °C**. Explain your answer.

....

....

....

[3]

[Total 8 marks]

Exam Practice Tip

When you're plotting graphs, it's important to be accurate. All your data points need to be correctly plotted, so use a nice, sharp pencil to plot the points and make life easier for yourself by drawing a graph that takes up as much of the available space as possible.

Score:

8

Section 1 — The Nature and Variety of Living Organisms

Human Nutrition

1   Fat is a vital component of a healthy diet.

a) Describe a test that could be used to determine whether fat is present in a sample of food. Include details of a positive result.

....

....

....

[2]

The digestion of fat and the absorption of its products can be affected by a range of disorders.

b) One of these disorders is tropical sprue, which causes flattening of the villi in the small intestine. Explain how tropical sprue may affect the absorption of fat.

....

....

....

[2]

Another disorder that can affect fat digestion and absorption is pancreatitis. In this disorder, the pancreas secretes fewer enzymes than it normally would.

c) i) Explain why people with pancreatitis might produce fatty faeces.

....

....

....

....

[3]

ii) Pancreatitis can be treated with enzyme supplements. People need to take these tablets at every meal, with a cold drink. Suggest why the tablets should not be taken with a hot drink.

....

....

[1]

iii) People with chronic pancreatitis are at greater risk of developing an obstruction in the tubes that connect the gallbladder to the small intestine. Explain how this could lead to weight loss.

....

....

....

....

[4]

[Total 12 marks]

2 Marathon runners often adapt their diets to help improve their performance. For example, they may increase their carbohydrate or protein intake.

a) An endurance runner is preparing for a marathon.
The day before the marathon she eats meals high in starch. Suggest why.

....

....

[1]

b) Another marathon runner has had part of his small intestine removed following an injury.
He has since struggled to build muscle strength whilst training. Suggest why.

....

....

....

....

....

[4]

The table shows a male marathon runner's energy requirements on a rest day (when he is not training) and on marathon day.

	Rest day	Marathon day
Energy required (kcal)	2500	3450

c) Calculate the percentage increase in energy required by the marathon runner on marathon day, compared to on a rest day.

....%

[2]

[Total 7 marks]

3 Which row in the table correctly describes a protein?

	Elements that a protein consists of	Causes biuret solution to turn
A ☐	carbon, hydrogen, oxygen	brick red
B ☐	carbon, hydrogen, oxygen, nitrogen	blue
C ☐	carbon, hydrogen, nitrogen	pink
D ☐	carbon, hydrogen, oxygen, nitrogen	pink

[Total 1 mark]

4 A group of students are investigating the nutritional value of some junk foods.

a) A student wants to compare the glucose content of crisps and marshmallows.
Describe how he could do this.

take 5cm³ ~~cots~~ g crisps & Marshmallows and place them
in test tube. Place the tube in 75°c water bath for five
minutes then remove and add Benedicts. If present it will change
from blue to red. [4]

A second student wanted to compare the energy content of crisps and marshmallows.
The results of her experiment are shown in the table below.

	Type of food	
	Crisp	Marshmallow
Mass of food (g)	0.20	0.24
Energy in food (J)	2436	2400

b) Describe a method the student could have used to obtain the results shown in the table.

- For crisp & Marshmallow onto Non-reactive metal spike
- Place over bunsen burner until they are a-light
- Once on fire place under test tube containing 20cm³ g
water and measure the temperature change g the water
until it cannot be re-lid. [5]

c) Using the results shown in the table, calculate the difference in the
energy content per gram of crisps and marshmallows.

12180 - 10,000 = 2180   2180   J/g
[2]

d) State **two** things the student should have done during her experiment to make sure that
her results were valid.
1. Place the fire ~~away~~ the same distance away from the water
2. insulate the test tube
[2]

[Total 13 marks]

Exam Practice Tip

Make sure you answer all the questions in an exam that you can — don't leave any blank if
you can avoid it, particularly the multiple choice questions. With these, if you don't know the
answer, try to narrow down your options by process of elimination before having a guess.

Score: ☐
33

Section 2 — Human Nutrition

Plant Nutrition and Transport

1   In the 17th century, a scientist called Jan Baptista van Helmont carried out an experiment to investigate plant growth. He grew a willow tree for 5 years in a pot of soil. During this time, the only thing he added to the soil was water. He weighed the pot and shoot at the start of the experiment and again after 5 years. He found that the pot and soil had lost barely any mass, but the tree had gained around 75 kg in mass. He concluded that plants must only need water in order to increase in mass.

a) Explain why van Helmont's conclusion is incorrect.

....

....
[1]

A scientific study recreated van Helmont's experiment over a 5-year period. In the study, three trees were grown outside, each in a different part of the UK. The results of the study are below.

	Initial mass of pot and soil (kg)	Final mass of pot and soil (kg)	% change in mass of pot and soil	Initial mass of tree (kg)	Final mass of tree (kg)	% change in mass of tree
Location A	35.1	34.9	− 0.6	2.1	22.2	957.1
Location B	42.0	41.9	− 0.2	3.4	67.2	1876.5
Location C	33.7	33.0	− 2.1	2.0	44.4	

b) i) Calculate the mean percentage change in mass for all the trees after 5 years.

mean = ...%
[3]

ii) The scientists controlled as many variables as they could in order to get valid results. Give **two** variables that the scientists should have controlled.

1. ....

2. ....
[2]

iii) The scientists predicted that the tree in Location **B** would increase in mass more than the tree in Location **A**.
Suggest **one** reason which may have led them to make this prediction. Explain your answer.

....

....

....
[2]

[Total 8 marks]

2   A student investigated the effect of light intensity on the rate of photosynthesis. She set up the experiment shown in the diagram and recorded the volume of oxygen collected in the syringe after 5 minutes. The light intensity was altered by moving the lamp away from the pondweed. The experiment was repeated three times at each distance from the lamp. The results are shown in the table below.

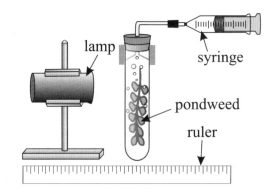

Distance of pondweed from the lamp (cm)	Volume of gas produced (cm³)			
	Test 1	Test 2	Test 3	Mean
5	11.4	14.2	13.6	13.1
10	13.0	14.5	12.5	13.3
20	11.5	12.0	11.5	11.7
30	9.0	8.5	10.0	9.2
40	7.0	8.0	6.0	7.0
50	6.5	5.5	4.5	5.5
60	1.0	2.0	1.5	1.5

a) At which distance from the lamp are the readings most precise? Explain your answer.

Distance: .... cm

Explanation: ....
....

[2]

b) Suggest **one** reason why the mean volume of gas produced at 5 cm is very similar to the mean volume of gas produced at 10 cm.

....

....

[1]

c) The table on the right gives information about three different types of bulb the student could have used in her lamp. Suggest which type of bulb the student should have used to increase the validity of her results. Explain your answer.

Type of bulb	Temperature of bulb when in use (°C)
Incandescent	168
CFL	55
LED	31

Type of bulb: ....

Explanation: ....

....

....

[3]

[Total 6 marks]

Score:

14

More Plant Nutrition and Transport

1   A student carried out an experiment to investigate the importance of light in photosynthesis. He placed a potted plant in a dark cupboard. After a few days, he partially covered one of its leaves with a black strip of paper and placed the plant on a sunny windowsill. After a few hours, he removed the paper, boiled the leaf in water for 10 minutes, then in alcohol for 10 minutes. He rinsed the leaf in cold water before adding a few drops of iodine solution to the leaf.

a) Explain why keeping the plant in the dark for a few days before starting the experiment helped to increase the validity of the student's results.

....

....

....

....

[3]

b) State the purpose of the black strip of paper which was used to partially cover the leaf.

....

[1]

c) Explain why the student boiled the leaf in water and then in alcohol.

....

....

....

[2]

d) Predict what happened when the student added iodine solution to the leaf. Justify your answer.

....

....

....

....

[3]

[Total 9 marks]

2   *Pythium aphanidermatum* is a pathogen that can infect the roots of a plant, leading to the destruction of many of the root hair cells.

a) Explain how *Pythium* infection may disrupt the transpiration stream.

....

....

....

[2]

b) Give **one** reason why plants infected with *Pythium* might show signs of nutrient deficiency.

....

....

[1]

[Total 3 marks]

3   A study was carried out to investigate the effect of light intensity on the rate of transpiration in two varieties of palm tree. One is native to the Middle East, the other grows in South Asia.

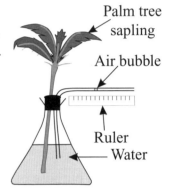

Palm tree sapling
Air bubble
Ruler
Water

- A scientist took a young sapling of the Middle Eastern tree and secured it inside a flask with a tube attached, as shown in the diagram.
- She used a lamp to control the light intensity the plant was exposed to.
- She investigated the rate of transpiration by recording how far an air bubble in the tube moved in a set period of time.
- She repeated the experiment at different light intensities and then repeated the whole experiment with the South Asian sapling.
- She controlled the humidity and the temperature throughout the experiment.
- Her results are shown in the table below.

	Middle Eastern Palm Tree					South Asian Palm Tree				
Light intensity (lux × 1000)	25	50	75	100	125	25	50	75	100	125
Distance moved by bubble (mm)	4	7	10	10	10	8	12	14	15	15

a) Plot a graph of the data in the table to show the results for both palm trees. You should draw and label **two** separate curves of best fit.

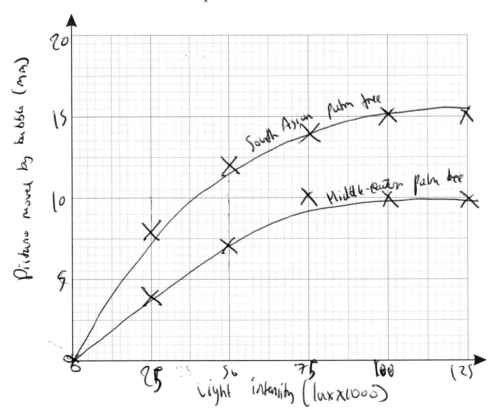

[6]

Section 3 — Plant Nutrition and Transport

b) It was important that the total surface area of both saplings' leaves was approximately the same. Explain why.

To allow the same amount volume of water being transpired in both plants

[3]

c) Give **one** way in which the scientist could improve the validity of the results.

Control the CO_2 and O_2 concentrations of the trees

[1]

The palm trees both have adaptations that make them suited to their environment.
The table below shows the average humidity for two regions in which the palm trees are found.

	Average Humidity (%)
Iraq (Middle East)	43
Bangladesh (South Asia)	78

d) Using your knowledge of leaf structure and the process of transpiration, explain the results of the study, shown on the previous page. As part of your explanation, include the information provided in the table above.

- South Asian palm tree is able to transpire out a higher rate
↳ This is due to it being adapted to its own area of high humidity. Meaning it will have a higher count of stomata, as humidity decreases transpiration
↳ As the plant is now in a hot lab environment which is less humid but still has the same number of stomata, the South Asian tree will be able to transpire at a higher rate

[6]

[Total 16 marks]

Section 3 — Plant Nutrition and Transport

Paper 2

Respiration and Gas Exchange

1   In humans, gas exchange in the lungs can be affected by various conditions.
For example, Chronic Obstructive Pulmonary Disease (COPD) describes a group of lung
conditions, including emphysema and bronchitis. Emphysema causes the structural shape of
the alveoli to break down, and bronchitis causes the bronchi to become inflamed and narrow.

a) Suggest how these changes in the lungs may affect gas exchange in people with COPD.

....

....

....
[2]

b) i)   At rest, patient A takes 2250 breaths in 2.5 hours, and patient B takes 750 breaths
in 30 minutes. Calculate the average breathing rate in breaths per minute for both patients.

Patient **A**: .... breaths per minute

Patient **B**: .... breaths per minute
[2]

ii) Which patient is more likely to have COPD? Explain your answer.

Patient: ....

Explanation: ....

....
[1]

In the lungs, white blood cells produce enzymes in response to infections and toxins such as
cigarette smoke. These enzymes help white blood cells to break down proteins in bacteria causing
an infection. However, the enzymes can also damage proteins that make up the cells in the lungs.

AAT is a protein that works in the lungs to limit the effect of these enzymes.
Some people have an inherited disorder known as a AAT deficiency (AATD).
People with this disorder often produce lower levels of AAT.

c) i)   People with AATD have an increased risk of developing COPD. Suggest why.

....

....
[2]

ii) Smoking is known to increase the risk of developing COPD in people with AATD.
Suggest why.

....

....
[2]

[Total 9 marks]

2 The respiratory system differs between animals. For example, unlike humans, crocodiles do not have a diaphragm. Instead, their liver is attached to their hip bones by a strong muscle called the diaphragmaticus. When the diaphragmaticus contracts, the liver is pulled backwards towards the tail. This helps to bring air into the lungs. The diagram below shows a simplified view of a crocodile's mid-section. The crocodile's ribcage and most of its internal organs are not shown.

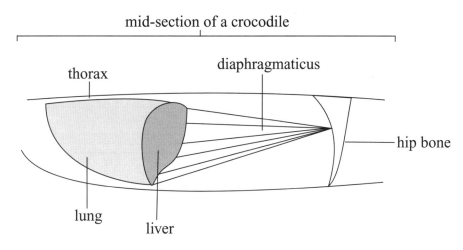

a) i) Suggest and explain how the movement of the liver helps to draw air into the crocodile's lungs.

....

....

....

[2]

ii) Injury to the diaphragmaticus does not completely prevent a crocodile from breathing. What does this suggest about the mechanism of breathing in crocodiles?

....

....

[1]

Despite the differences in the respiratory systems of crocodiles and humans, there are also many similarities. For example, the same membranes surround the lungs of both humans and crocodiles. Like humans, crocodiles also have a trachea that is supported by stiff rings of cartilage.

b) Suggest why it is important that the trachea is supported in this way.

....

....

....

[2]

c) Name the membranes that surround the lungs in both humans and crocodiles.

....

[1]

[Total 6 marks]

Section 4 — Respiration and Gas Exchange

3 A scientist was measuring the effects of exercise on respiration. He asked a male volunteer to jog for 10 minutes on a treadmill. The speed of the treadmill was increased over the course of the 10 minutes, so that the volunteer was gradually working harder, until at the end he felt unable to do any more exercise. The graph below shows the oxygen consumption (the amount of oxygen used by the body per minute) of the volunteer during the exercise.

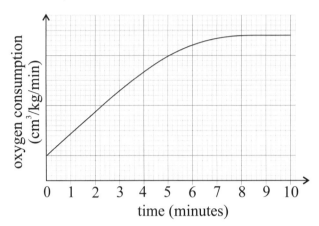

a) Describe how the volunteer's oxygen consumption changed during the exercise.

....

....

[2]

b) For every oxygen molecule that the volunteer consumed during exercise, how many molecules of carbon dioxide did he produce?

☐ **A** 1

☐ **B** 2

☐ **C** 4

☐ **D** 6

[1]

c) In the final two minutes of the exercise, the volunteer was respiring anaerobically.

i) Describe the relative yields of ATP produced in aerobic and anaerobic respiration.

....

....

[1]

ii) Explain how the scientist may know when the volunteer was respiring anaerobically by looking at the graph.

....

....

....

[2]

[Total 6 marks]

Score:

21

Section 4 — Respiration and Gas Exchange

More Respiration and Gas Exchange

1 Plants can adapt to changes in their environmental conditions. If a plant is grown in an artificial environment with a very low level of carbon dioxide, new leaves grow which have a higher stomatal density. A student investigated how this change in stomatal density affects gas exchange in normal atmospheric conditions.

The student used two plants in her investigation:

- Plant **1** had been grown in an artificial environment with a very low concentration of carbon dioxide.
- Plant **2** had been grown in normal atmospheric conditions.

The student took a fresh leaf with the same total surface area from both plants and placed them into separate, sealed test tubes containing equal volumes of atmospheric air and orange hydrogencarbonate indicator (as shown in the diagram below). She exposed both test tubes to the same high light intensity and measured the time taken for the indicator to change colour.

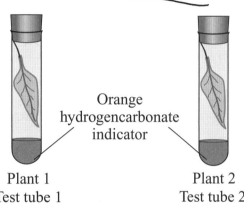

Orange
hydrogencarbonate
indicator

Plant 1   Plant 2
Test tube 1   Test tube 2

a) i) Predict the colour change that the student would have seen in both test tubes.
Explain your answer.

— Test tube 1 will be purple as it will contain less CO_2
— Test tube 2 will be yellow as it will have a
higher concentration of CO_2

[3]

ii) Predict the test tube in which the colour change would have occurred fastest.
Explain your answer.

Test tube 1 as Plant 1 will have a higher
number of stomata allowing for a higher rate
of photosynthesis

[3]

b) Other than those described in the method above, identify **two** variables in this investigation that should have been controlled.

1. *Temperature* *(Health)*

2. *Age of leaves*

[2]

c) Besides a high stomatal density, suggest **one** other adaptation plants might develop in response to a low level of carbon dioxide in the atmosphere. Give a reason for your answer.

Increase the for Surface area of the leaves so that they are able to absorb more CO₂

[2]

d) The imprints of some fossilised leaves show that ancient plants had much higher stomatal densities than modern leaves.
Suggest **one** thing this tells us about the atmosphere at the time these plants were alive.

Atmosphere of at the time had a lower CO₂ concentration in the atmosphere

[1]

[Total 11 marks]

2 The graph shows the mean net oxygen consumption for two organisms (**A** and **B**), over 24 hours, in the UK in spring. Organism **A** is an animal and organism **B** is a plant.

a) Suggest and explain why the mean net oxygen consumption for organism **A** is lower at 12 am than at 12 pm.

- The animal could be asleep meaning it will not be engaging in as much Metabolic activity and therefore not be utilising as much oxygen for respiration

[3]

b) Describe and explain the mean net oxygen consumption for organism **B** between 7 am and 12 pm.

- The consumption is negative as the plant is producing the oxygen through photosynthesis, which is heightened during the day due to a higher light intensity

[2]

[Total 5 marks]

Exam Practice Tip

If you're asked about the variables that would need to be controlled in an experiment you're unfamiliar with, start by thinking about what it is you're changing (the independent variable) and what it is you're measuring (the dependent variable). Then have a think about anything else that might affect the results — these factors are the control variables and need to be kept the same. Sorted.

Score:

16

Blood and Organs

20   2

1 Blood is constantly pumped around the body and performs many important functions.

a) 1991 cm³ of blood passed through one artery in 5.5 minutes.
   Calculate the volume of blood that would flow through this artery in one day.

.... cm³/day
[2]

b) Anaemia is a condition that can be caused by a lack of haemoglobin in red blood cells.
   Suggest why a symptom of this condition is feeling tired and weak.

....

....

....

....
[3]

c) HIV is a virus. It destroys the white blood cells that activate lymphocytes.
   Explain why someone with an untreated HIV infection might be vulnerable to other diseases.

....

....

....

....
[3]

Blood plasma carries many different proteins around the body.
Some of these proteins and their roles are outlined below.

Factor V (a protein that helps to
convert prothrombin to thrombin)

Prothrombin ————————————————→ Thrombin (an enzyme
(a protein)   that activates platelets)

d) Suggest why surgery might be risky for a person with a deficiency in Factor V.

....

....

....

....
[3]

[Total 11 marks]

The heart is responsible for the circulation of blood around the body.
The diagram below shows the structure of the heart.

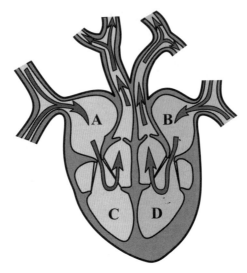

a) Which of the following statements about the diagram above is **true**?

☐ **A** Blood enters Chamber **A** through the aorta.

☐ **B** Blood leaves Chamber **B** through the tricuspid valve.

☒ **C** Blood leaves Chamber **C** through the pulmonary artery.

☐ **D** Blood enters Chamber **D** from the right atrium.

[1]

In comparison to non-athletes, elite athletes often have an enlarged left ventricle
and a thicker left ventricle wall.

b) i) Explain a possible benefit of the structural differences in the heart of an elite athlete,
when compared to a non-athlete.

....

....

....

....

[3]

ii) Describe the mechanism that causes an athlete's heart rate to increase during a race.

....

....

....

....

[3]

[Total 7 marks]

3 There are many diseases that can affect the heart's function.

a) Mitral stenosis occurs when the bicuspid (mitral) valve becomes narrowed.
Suggest why this condition could lead to an enlarged left atrium.

....

....

[2]

b) Angina is a condition that causes chest pain due to reduced blood flow to the heart muscle.
Suggest **two** factors that could increase the risk of a person developing angina.
Explain why each of the factors you have suggested could lead to angina.

Factor 1: ......Smoking..

Explanation: ......Increases heart rate → More plaque → less blood to heart.....................

Factor 2: ......Eating too Much saturated fats...

Explanation: ......buildup of plaque in blood vessels → less blood to the heart..................

[4]

[Total 6 marks]

4 Meningitis is a life-threatening disease that affects the brain and spinal cord.
The disease can be caused by bacterial, viral or fungal pathogens. In 2015,
a new vaccine was introduced in the UK to protect babies against a particular
strain of bacteria that causes meningitis — meningococcal B bacteria.

Explain why the vaccine gives a baby immunity against meningococcal B bacteria but not
meningococcal C bacteria.

....

....

....

....

....

....

....

....

....

....

[Total 6 marks]

Paper 2

Section 5 — Blood and Organs

Paper 2

5 The level of ADH in the blood fluctuates to control the water content of the body.

a) Explain why the level of ADH in the blood may increase after exercise.

....

....

....

....

[3]

b) Diabetes insipidus is a rare condition that disrupts the usual control of water balance.
People with this condition often stop producing ADH. Explain why a person with diabetes *not diabetes mellitus*
insipidus may need to drink more each day than a person without the condition.

....

....

....

....

[3]

[Total 6 marks]

6 Glomerulonephritis is the name given to a group of diseases which damage the walls of the glomerular capillaries. This may lead to a reduction in the rate at which blood is filtered through the glomeruli.

a) Suggest **two** possible problems that glomerulonephritis may cause.

1. ...... body not able to reabsorb as much minerals & glucose.

2. ...... Infection y blood stream ....

[2]

The volume of blood reaching the glomeruli to be filtered depends on the heart rate.

b) In the average person, the heart beats 75 times per minute and 70 cm^3 of blood is pumped out of the left ventricle with each beat. Approximately 20% of the total blood pumped out of the left ventricle each minute goes to the kidneys to be filtered.
Calculate the volume of blood sent to the kidneys every hour.

.... cm^3 per hour
[2]

[Total 4 marks]

Exam Practice Tip

Don't panic if you're unfamiliar with some of the information given in a question — for example, you're not expected to know about meningitis or glomerulonephritis. To get the top grades, you need to be able to read new information and relate it to material you have studied.

Score: ☐

40

Section 5 — Blood and Organs

Human Coordination and Response

1 Every Boxing Day, hundreds of people in the UK take part in charity events that involve them briefly running into the sea. When people taking part in the charity events leave the water, parts of their skin may appear grey. This is because there is a reduction in blood flow to the surface of the skin.

a) Explain the purpose of this response.

- To conserve energy and heat in the vital organs by redistributing blood away from the skin.

[2]

b) Explain in detail how being in the water leads to this response.

- The body responds to the stimulus of the colder water

→ first the receptors in the skin then relay this information to a sensory neurone, which transmits this to the central nervous system

- The CNS responds by ~~decreasing~~ redirecting blood flow from the skin to the vital organs by alerting the heart through a motor neurone

[5]

[Total 7 marks]

2 Some stimuli are interpreted by the brain as being painful. When receptors detect these stimuli, impulses are passed to the spinal cord and then to the brain. Opioid drugs can relieve pain, partly because they prevent the release of neurotransmitters from certain sensory neurones.

With reference to synapses, explain how opioids can relieve pain.

Opioids block neurotransmitters from crossing a synapse to from one neurone to another. This prevents a signal being sent to the CNS, preventing an effect

[Total 3 marks]

24

3   A person's reaction time is the amount of time it takes them to respond to a stimulus — for example, the amount of time it takes them to press a button when they see a shape on a computer screen.
A student hypothesises that drinking coffee will speed up a person's reaction time.

Design an investigation to test this hypothesis.
Include details of the method the student could use. Write your answer in full sentences.

....

....

....

....

....

....

....

....

....

....

[Total 6 marks]

4   Light enters the eye through the pupil. In bright light, the pupil gets smaller to prevent the eye from being damaged. This is known as the iris reflex. It is controlled by the nervous system.

a) Describe how the iris reflex is likely to occur.

The stimulus y an increased amount y light is detected by the retina and optic nerve which then relays this information through a sensory neurone to the central nervous system. The central nervous system then responds by sending a signal through a motor neurone to the pupil and iris causing it to contract.

....

....

....

....

[6]

Section 6 — Coordination and Response

b) The iris reflex may be used by doctors to assess whether there is any damage
to the nerves connecting the brain and the eye in coma patients.

Predict whether an unconscious patient without damage to these nerves would show
an iris reflex when a bright light is shone into their eye. Explain your answer.

The patients pupil would get smaller, as it's a
reflex and not a consious change

[1]

c) Suggest and explain **one** reason why the iris reflex is controlled by
the nervous system rather than the hormonal system.

- More Precise
- faster response

[2]

[Total 9 marks]

5 Some people develop visual defects which cause problems when focusing on near or distant objects.

a) Pseudomyopia is a temporary condition caused by prolonged focus on near objects,
such as a computer screen. In pseudomyopia, the ciliary muscles do not relax.

Explain how pseudomyopia may affect a person's vision when they try to focus on distant objects.

- The Ciliary muscles are not relaxing, which in-turn does
not allow the Suspensory ligaments to contract
The lens does not go thin, which Lea means that the
light is not refracted correctly.

[3]

b) Laser eye surgery is one possible treatment for vision defects.
In this process, a laser is used to heat and reshape the cornea.

Suggest why laser eye surgery can improve a person's vision.

[2]

[Total 5 marks]

Exam Practice Tip

When you're faced with a question in the exam that requires a longer answer, don't just jump
straight in and start writing the first thing that springs to mind. Roughly plan what points you
want to make first, either in your head or on the exam paper (you should cross out anything you
don't want marked afterwards). This will help you to make sure you don't miss anything important.

Score:

30

Plant Coordination and Response

1   A group of students investigated the concept of geotropism in
     germinating pea seedlings. They used a piece of apparatus called
     a clinostat, which suspended and slowly rotated the seedlings over
     several days. The experimental set up is shown in the diagram below.

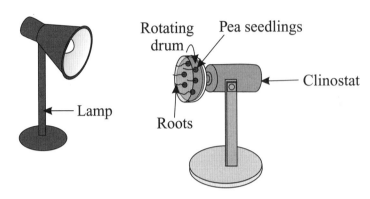

a) Describe the normal geotropic response of plant roots.

     ....

     ....
                                                                                              [1]

b) Explain why it was important to keep the lamp on and in the
    same position throughout the experiment.

     ....

     ....

     ....
                                                                                              [2]

c) Which of the following would be a suitable control for this experiment?

     ☐   **A**   Pea seedlings grown on a clinostat which is not rotating.

     ☐   **B**   Pea seedlings grown on a clinostat that is rotating in the opposite direction.

     ☐   **C**   A rotating clinostat with no pea seedlings present.

     ☐   **D**   A rotating clinostat with the lamp switched off.
                                                                                              [1]

d) Explain why the roots of the seedlings in this experiment grew horizontally.

     ....

     ....
                                                                                              [1]

                                                                                    [Total 5 marks]

                                                                        Score: ☐

                                                                              5

Section 6 — Coordination and Response

Reproduction

1 The fruit and seeds of an ancient plant called *Silene* were buried by animals and frozen in underground ice for over 30 000 years. Scientists attempted to grow new *Silene* plants from the seeds, but although the seeds germinated, they did not develop into mature plants. The scientists were successful in growing cloned plants from the fruit tissue.

a) i) Suggest **two** reasons why the seeds did not germinate during the 30 000 years.

1. ....

2. ....

[2]

ii) Suggest **one** reason why the germinated seeds may not have been able to develop into a mature plant.

....

....

[1]

b) Cloning plants from fruit tissue is a form of artificial asexual reproduction. State **one** difference between cloning plants from fruit tissue and growing them from seed.

....

....

[1]

c) i) *Silene* produces large, white flowers that are pollinated by insects. Which row in the table shows characteristics of insect-pollinated flowers?

	Strong scent	Number of pollen grains produced	Surface of pollen grains	Surface of stigma
A ☐	Yes	Moderate	Sticky	Sticky
B ☐	No	Moderate	Smooth	Feathery
C ☐	Yes	Very high	Sticky	Feathery
D ☐	No	Very high	Smooth	Sticky

[1]

ii) Most of the flowers produced on the ancient *Silene* plant were female. Which structure would be absent from these flowers?

☐ **A** Anther

☐ **B** Ovary

☐ **C** Style

☐ **D** Stigma

[1]

[Total 6 marks]

2   Progesterone is a sex hormone involved in the menstrual cycle.

In a study, scientists looked at the secretion patterns of progesterone.
The blood concentration of progesterone was measured in three women over an eight-week period.
The results are shown in the graph below.

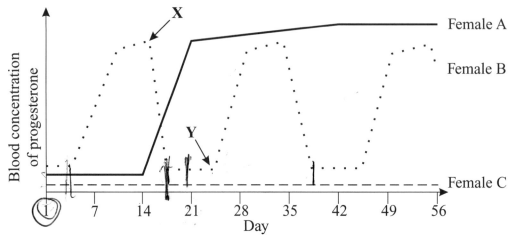

a) Estimate the duration of **one** menstrual cycle in Female **B**.

.... 21 .... days

[1]

Paper 2

b) Explain how the level of **LH** in the blood will differ between points **X** and **Y** on the graph above.

Point X will have less LH as the progesterone
levels are high, however at Y the levels are
low

[2]

c) Female **A** became pregnant during the study.
Suggest an explanation for the secretion pattern shown for Female **A** from day 21.

LH and FSH levels could decrease because
there is a fertilised egg. meaning progesterone levels must
stay heightered and also maintain the uterus lining

[2]

d) Once a woman has experienced the menopause, she will no longer ovulate.
Explain the secretion pattern for Female **C**, who experienced the menopause many years prior
to this study.

....

....

....

[2]

[Total 7 marks]

Exam Practice Tip

When faced with a graph in an exam question, don't just glance at it then jump straight in.
Take a minute or so to study the introductory information, the axis labels, the units, the key and any
patterns in the data. You can always make notes on the page to highlight the most important bits.

Score: [ ]

13

Section 7 — Reproduction and Inheritance   [ ] [ ] 😊 [ ]

DNA and Inheritance

1   Cells in the pancreas produce the hormone insulin. Insulin is a protein.

Describe the process by which the insulin gene is used to produce insulin in the cells of the pancreas.

....

....

....

....

....

....

....

....

....

....

[Total 6 marks]

2   Problems with meiosis can lead to health disorders. The photograph on the right shows the chromosomes in a cell of an embryo with Down syndrome.

a) Using the photograph, suggest how the set of chromosomes in an individual with Down syndrome differs from an individual without Down syndrome.

....

....

....

....

[1]

b) How many of the other cells in the embryo would you expect to contain the difference referred to in part a)? Explain your answer.

....

....

....

[2]

Section 7 — Reproduction and Inheritance

The table shows three other syndromes and information about the possible chromosomes that could result.

Syndrome	Number of chromosomes	Sex chromosomes
Turner syndrome	45	X only
Rett syndrome	46	XX
Klinefelter syndrome	47	XXY

c) If the sex chromosomes fail to separate in meiosis, an egg cell with XX or a sperm cell with XY may be formed. Suggest how this could lead to **one** of the syndromes in **Table 1**.

....

....

....

[2]

[Total 5 marks]

3   Molecules called mRNA and tRNA are involved in converting the sequence of bases in DNA into a sequence of amino acids in a protein.

The table shows the amino acids coded for by some mRNA codons.
The diagram shows two tRNA molecules, each with an amino acid attached.
The anticodon for the tRNA molecule carrying the amino acid serine is also shown.

mRNA codon	Amino Acid
GUU	valine
GUG	valine
AGC	serine
CGA	arginine
GAU	aspartic acid
CCU	proline
CCC	proline

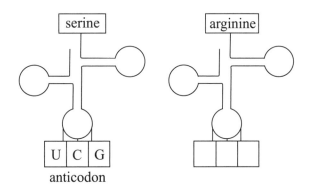

a) Using the information given above, identify the anticodon sequence of arginine's tRNA molecule.

....

[1]

The diagram on the right shows the simplified structure of a region of an organism's genome.

b) i) Explain why a mutation at **position 2** could change the organism's phenotype.

....

....

....

[3]

Section 7 — Reproduction and Inheritance

Paper 2

ii) Use information from the table above to explain why a mutation at **position 2** might **not** affect the organism's phenotype.

....

....

....

[3]

[Total 7 marks]

4 Sickle cell anaemia is an inherited disease that affects the development of the haemoglobin protein. This can cause red blood cells to distort into crescent shapes. Haemoglobin is made up of four protein subunits. The *HBB* gene provides instructions for making two of these subunits.

a) The table below shows the base sequence for the first six amino acids coded for by the *HBB* gene.

base sequence	GTG	CAC	CTG	ACT	CCT	GAG
amino acid	Val	His	Leu	Thr	Pro	Glu

There are 423 more bases after this in the gene.
Calculate how many amino acids the *HBB* gene codes for.

.... amino acids

[2]

The allele that causes sickle cell anaemia is recessive.
A family with a history of sickle cell anaemia consults a genetic counsellor for advice.
Their family pedigree is shown below.

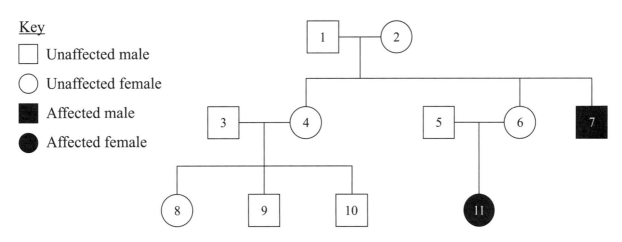

b) i) Explain how the genetic counsellor knew from the family pedigree above that individuals 1 and 2 were heterozygous for the allele that causes sickle cell anaemia.

....

....

....

....

[2]

Section 7 — Reproduction and Inheritance

ii) Individual 4 in the diagram claimed that she could not be a carrier of the recessive allele, because she had already had three unaffected children. The genetic counsellor says that this may not be true. Suggest **two** explanations as to why individual 4's statement may not be true.

1. ....

....

2. ....

....

[4]

[Total 8 marks]

5   Autosomal recessive polycystic kidney disease (ARPKD) is an inherited condition that causes the kidneys and liver to develop abnormally. Over time, the condition can cause a severe loss of kidney function. Around 0.005% of babies are born with ARPKD.

a) Approximately 7.75×10^5 babies were born in the UK in 2016.
How many of these would be expected to have ARPKD?

  ☐ **A** 4

  ☐ **B** 39

  ☐ **C** 386

  ☐ **D** 3875

[1]

b) A healthy couple are expecting a baby. Genetic tests reveal that the father is a carrier of the recessive allele for ARPKD but the mother is not.

Use a genetic diagram to determine the probability of the couple having a child with ARPKD.

Your diagram should show the genotypes of the parents and their gametes, as well as the possible genotypes and phenotypes of their offspring.

Use '**D**' to represent the dominant allele and '**d**' to represent the recessive allele.

Probability of child being born with ARPKD = ...
[4]

[Total 5 marks]

Exam Practice Tip

You've really got to learn all the scientific words related to this topic (dominant, recessive, heterozygous, etc.). Not only could you be asked to define them in the exam, it's assumed you'll know what the terms mean when they're used in questions. It's hard to get the right answer if you don't know what the question's asking you, so make sure you've learnt all the vocab.

Score: ☐
31

Evolution

1   A scientist investigated the evolution of antibiotic resistance in bacteria. He spread
a bacterial growth medium on to a rectangular plate and divided the plate into five
sections, **A** to **E**. He then added a low concentration of antibiotic to sections **B** and
D, and a high concentration of the same antibiotic to section **C**. Sections **A** and **E**
did not have any antibiotic added. A side view of this plate is shown below.

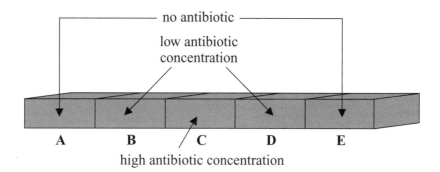

On the first day of the investigation, the scientist added an identical volume of bacteria to
sections **A** and **E**. The plate was then incubated and observed for 14 days.
The observations are shown below.

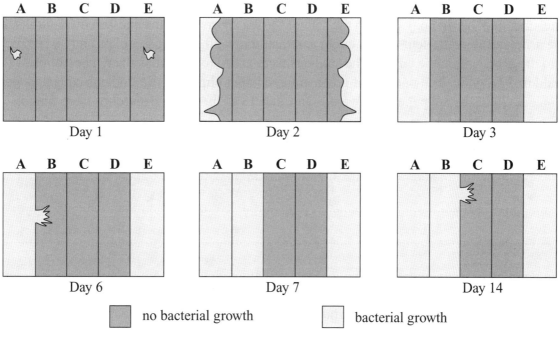

a) Suggest **one** reason why it is advantageous for the bacteria to grow into a new section of the plate.

   ....

   ....

   [1]

b) Explain the appearance of the plate when it is observed on Day **3**.

   ....

   ....

   ....

   [2]

c) Explain the difference in the appearance of sections **B** and **D** on Day **6**.

....

....

....

....

....

[4]

d) Predict how the results would be different if the bacteria were exposed to
ionising radiation at the start of the experiment. Explain your answer.

....

....

....

....

[3]

[Total 10 marks]

2 A teacher took her biology class to the school's grass sports field for a lesson on natural selection.
She arranged some students into a circle and then threw 30 green paperclips and 30 red paperclips
onto the grass within the circle. The students were asked to collect as many paperclips as they
could in 5 seconds. The number of green and red paper clips that the students collected were then
counted. 25 of the red paperclips were found, and 13 of the green paperclips were found.

a) Explain how this demonstration models part of the theory of evolution by natural selection.

....

....

....

....

[2]

b) Give **two** ways in which this demonstration does **not** fully model the theory of evolution by
natural selection.

1. ....

....

2. ....

....

[2]

[Total 4 marks]

Score:

14

Section 7 — Reproduction and Inheritance

Ecosystems and Biodiversity

1 A study was carried out to investigate competition between two beetle species, *Tribolium confusum* and *Tribolium castaneum*. The beetle species were studied under six different laboratory conditions, where both species were put together in the same environment and left until only one species remained. The surviving beetle species was the 'winner' of the competition. The graph below shows the outcome of the competition.

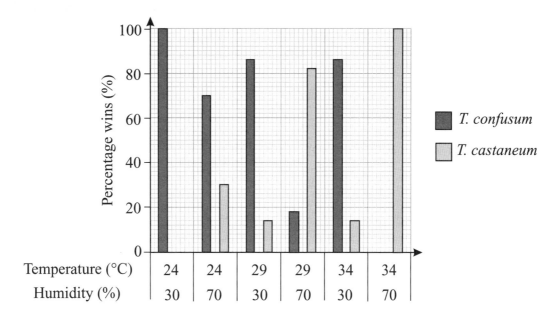

a) Another scientist repeated the experiment 18 times at 29 °C and 70% humidity. Calculate the number of times that *T. confusum* would be expected to win.

Number of times *T. confusum* expected to win = ...
[2]

b) Using the graph above, suggest which beetle species is more likely to live in a hot and humid habitat. Explain your answer.

....
[1]

c) *T. castaneum* is able to fly short distances whereas *T. confusum* is not. Based on this information, which species do you think would be more likely to survive if they were found together in a natural environment? Give **one** explanation for your answer.

....
[1]

d) *T. castaneum* are common pests amongst stored foods, so pesticides are often used to control this species. Suggest how this method of control could affect biodiversity in nearby areas of water.

....

....

....
[2]

[Total 6 marks]

Paper 2

2 A student investigated the distribution of different plant species on a beach. The data she collected is shown in the table below.

Distance from the sea (m)	Salt concentration of the soil (arbitrary units)	Species (% cover)					
		Sea couch	Marram grass	Sea holly	Restharrow	Bird's-foot trefoil	Bramble
50	20	5	0	0	0	0	0
100	18	10	30	0	0	0	0
150	17	5	10	10	0	0	0
250	14	0	10	5	5	5	0
350	12	0	5	5	20	5	10

a) Describe how the student could have collected the data shown in the table above.

....

....

....

....
[4]

b) Explain how the biodiversity of plant species on the beach correlates with distance from the sea.

....

....

....
[2]

c) Suggest an explanation for the distribution of sea couch.

....

....

....

....
[4]

d) Another student repeated the investigation on the same beach. His results were not the same as the first student's. Suggest **one** reason why the data in the table above may not be reproducible.

....

....
[1]

[Total 11 marks]

Score:

17

Section 8 — Ecology and the Environment

Energy Transfer in Ecosystems

1   The diagram below shows the primary and secondary consumer on a pyramid of biomass.

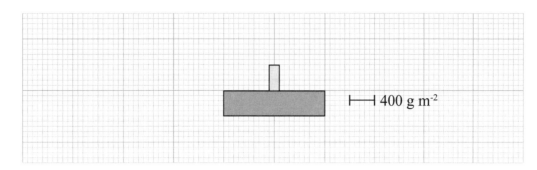

├──┤ 400 g m⁻²

a) The biomass of the producer is 5600 g m⁻².
    Draw the bar representing the producer onto the graph above.

[2]

b) Calculate the efficiency of biomass transfer between the producer and the primary consumer.
    Give your answer to 2 significant figures. Use the following equation:

$$\text{Efficiency} = \frac{\text{Biomass transferred to the next level}}{\text{Biomass available at the previous level}} \times 100$$

....%
[2]
[Total 4 marks]

2   The diagram shows independent organisms in a marine ecosystem.

Explain fully what would be likely
to happen to the number of zooplankton
and mullet if cod became extinct.

....

....

....

....

....

....

....

....

....

....

....

[Total 6 marks]

Section 8 — Ecology and the Environment

3   The diagram below represents the flow of energy
     through a community. Values are in kJ m⁻² yr⁻¹.

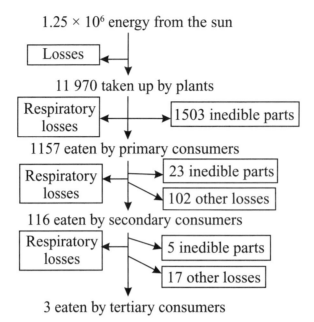

1.25 × 10⁶ energy from the sun

Losses

11 970 taken up by plants

Respiratory losses ←→ 1503 inedible parts

1157 eaten by primary consumers

Respiratory losses ← 23 inedible parts
                    ← 102 other losses

116 eaten by secondary consumers

Respiratory losses ← 5 inedible parts
                   ← 17 other losses

3 eaten by tertiary consumers

a) Using the diagram above, calculate the percentage of energy from the sun that is available to the tertiary consumers. Express your answer in standard form.

.... %
[2]

b) State whether there are likely to be more primary consumers or secondary consumers in the community shown above. Explain your answer.

....

....
[1]

c) 'Respiratory losses' represents the energy lost from the community through respiration. Explain how energy is lost through respiration.

....

....
[1]

d) Give **two** substances that could be included in 'other losses'.

1. ....

2. ....
[2]
[Total 6 marks]

Score:

16

Section 8 — Ecology and the Environment

Carbon and Nitrogen Cycles

1   A harvest mouse's diet includes seeds.

   a) At some point, some of the carbon in the seeds could have been part of another harvest mouse.
   Explain how the carbon could have become part of the seeds following the death of another mouse.

   ....

   ....

   ....

   ....

   ....

   [4]

   b) Seeds contain proteins. The harvest mouse takes these in and uses them to make proteins
   in its own body. Excess proteins in its diet are broken down in its body to form urea.

   Explain the role of bacteria in making the proteins that were taken in by
   the mouse available again to the plant that produced the seeds.

   ....

   ....

   ....

   ....

   ....

   ....

   ....

   ....

   ....

   ....

   ....

   ....

   [6]

   [Total 10 marks]

Paper 2

Exam Practice Tip

It's relatively easy to learn something like the nitrogen cycle off by heart — what's harder is applying
the facts you've learnt to new contexts. Just remember that whether you're writing about the
nitrogen cycle in the context of a farmer's field, a woodland or a river, the facts won't change.

Score:

10

Section 8 — Ecology and the Environment

Pollution

1   Human activity produces large amounts of greenhouse gases. The graph
below shows the UK's greenhouse gas emissions between 1990 and 2016.

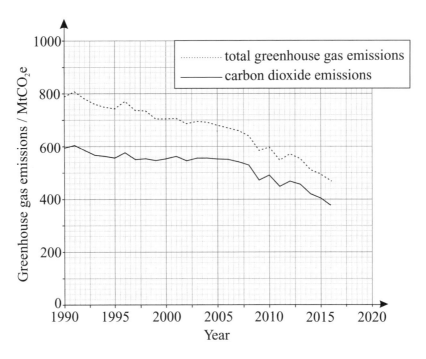

a) i)   Estimate what percentage of the total greenhouse gas emissions in **2016**
were carbon dioxide emissions.

.........................%
[2]

ii) Besides carbon dioxide, state **two** other gases that may
make up the total greenhouse gas emissions.

1. ....

2. ....
[2]

b) Between **2011** and **2016** nine coal power stations were closed. Suggest how these
closures could explain the trend shown on the graph for the **2011-2016** period.

....

....

....
[2]

c) Describe **one** environmental benefit of the overall trend shown on the graph.

....

....
[1]

[Total 7 marks]

Section 8 — Ecology and the Environment

2   A group of students carried out some fieldwork on a local river. They wanted to learn more about the effect of a tourist resort next to the river on the level of water pollution.

The students chose five sites along the river, and assessed the population size of two species that require high oxygen levels to survive (freshwater shrimp and stonefly nymph).
The tourist site was positioned between sites **2** and **3**. The students' data is plotted on the graph on the right.

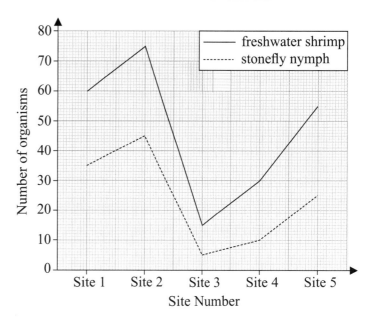

a) Calculate the percentage decrease in the population of freshwater shrimps between sites **2** and **3**.

........................%
[2]

The students also looked at algal growth. They found the highest level between sites **2** and **3**.

b) i) Explain **one** way in which the presence of the tourist resort could have led to increased algal growth.

....

....

....
[2]

ii) Use the information the students collected about algal growth to suggest an explanation for the change in population size of freshwater shrimp and stonefly nymph between sites **2** and **3**.

....

....

....

....
[3]
[Total 7 marks]

Exam Practice Tip

Don't be thrown by graphs that have more than one set of data plotted on them — use the key and double check you know which line represents which set of data before answering the questions.

Score:

14

Section 8 — Ecology and the Environment

Use of Biological Resources

1   A farmer is planning to alter conditions in his glasshouse to help increase the rate of photosynthesis of his crop. The current conditions in the farmer's glasshouse are shown in the table below. He is using the graph below to help him choose how to change the conditions.

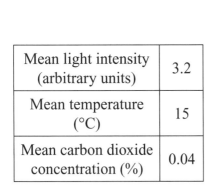

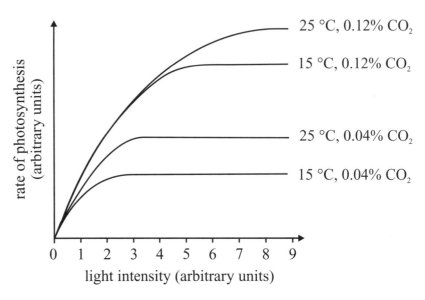

a) Suggest why the farmer wants to increase the rate of photosynthesis of his crop.

....

....

[2]

b) Sketch a line on the graph above to show the rate of photosynthesis at 15 °C and a carbon dioxide concentration of 0.08%.

[1]

c) The farmer is considering doing only one of the following to change conditions in his glasshouse:

A   Increasing the light intensity to 8 arbitrary units.
B   Increasing the temperature to 25 °C.
C   Increasing the carbon dioxide concentration to 0.12%.

Which **one** of the options, **A-C**, would be most beneficial to the farmer? Explain your answer.

Option: .... Explanation: ....

....

....

[3]

d) Explain why it would not be economical for the farmer to increase the temperature in his glasshouse to 25 °C **and** increase the carbon dioxide concentration to 0.12%.

....

....

[2]

[Total 8 marks]

2 Yeast is a useful microorganism that can be used in baking.

a) A baker is baking bread. She forgets to add yeast to the bread dough.
Explain why the dough does not rise.

....

....

....

[2]

b) Suggest **two** reasons why dough may not rise, even when yeast is added.

1. ....

2. ....

[2]

[Total 4 marks]

3 Yoghurt is produced using bacteria. The bacteria use lactose, the sugar found in milk, as an energy source to produce lactic acid via anaerobic respiration. This lowers the pH, which causes the milk to thicken and form yoghurt.

a) A student wants to investigate the effect of temperature on the rate of formation of yoghurt.
Design a laboratory experiment that the student could carry out to investigate this.
Include details of the method the student could use. Write your answer in full sentences.

....

....

....

....

....

....

....

....

....

....

....

....

....

[6]

44

Scientists carried out an experiment to measure the change in the number of bacteria in a fermenter over ten hours, during the production of a batch of yoghurt. The results are shown in the table on the right.

time / hours	number of bacteria in 1 cm³ / millions
0	4
2	6
4	7
6	10
8	18
10	6

b) Plot a graph on the grid below to show how the number of bacteria in 1 cm³ changed over the 10 hours in the fermenter. Join the points in your graph using straight lines.

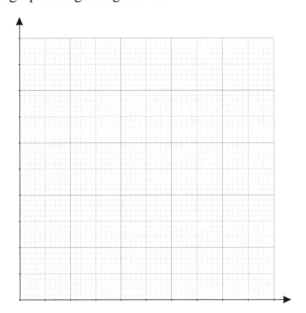

[4]

c) There is a dramatic fall in the number of bacteria towards the end of the 10-hour period.

   i) Suggest **one** possible reason for this decrease.

   ....

   ....

   [1]

   ii) Suggest **one** way in which the fermenter could be adjusted to prevent this from happening again in subsequent batch production.

   ....

   ....

   [1]

   [Total 12 marks]

Exam Practice Tip

Designing an experiment is tricky. Start by thinking about what it is you're going to measure (the dependent variable) and how you could go about accurately measuring it. Your answer should include details of repeat measurements if appropriate, as well as any variables to be controlled.

Score:

24

More on the Use of Biological Resources

1 *Bt* corn is a GM crop plant. It produces *Bt* toxin, a protein which kills corn borer insects that feed on the crop. The process developed to first make *Bt* corn involves two species of bacteria: *Bacillus thuringiensis*, which produces the *Bt* toxin, and *Agrobacterium tumefaciens*, which invades plant cells and inserts genes into the plant's DNA.

a) The following steps are part of the original process involved in making *Bt* corn.
   They are **not** in the correct order:

1. The corn plant is dipped into the colony of *Agrobacterium tumefaciens*, which inserts the *Bt* toxin gene into the corn plant's genome.
2. The *Bt* toxin gene is inserted into a bacterial plasmid.
3. The bacterial plasmid is inserted into *Agrobacterium tumefaciens*.
4. The toxin gene is isolated from the *Bacillus thuringiensis* genome.
5. The *Agrobacterium tumefaciens* is left to multiply.

   i) Identify the correct order of the steps above.

   ☐ **A** 5, 3, 4, 2, 1
   ☐ **B** 4, 2, 3, 5, 1
   ☐ **C** 4, 3, 5, 2, 1
   ☐ **D** 3, 5, 2, 1, 4

   [1]

   ii) Describe how the *Bt* toxin gene is isolated from the *Bacillus thuringiensis* genome.

   ....

   ....

   [1]

   iii) Explain why both the plasmid and *Agrobacterium tumefaciens*
       can be described as vectors in this process.

   ....

   ....

   ....

   [2]

b) The uptake of plasmids by bacteria is extremely inefficient. *Agrobacterium tumefaciens*
   is left to multiply on a growth medium that contains an antibiotic. As the bacteria divide,
   they replicate their DNA, including any plasmids they contain. Suggest an explanation for
   why a gene for antibiotic resistance is included in the same plasmid as the *Bt* gene.

   ....

   ....

   ....

   [2]

After the first *Bt* corn plants were developed, more *Bt* corn plants were produced via a plant breeding programme. The programme was started using plant tissue culture (micropropagation).

c) i) State **one** reason why tissue culture may have been used to create new lines of *Bt* corn plants.

....

....

[1]

ii) Describe a method that could have been used to grow more *Bt* corn plants via tissue culture.

....

....

....

....

....

[4]

[Total 11 marks]

2 On fish farms, fish are raised in enclosures and are often sold as food.
Much of the fish we eat today comes from fish farming rather than fishing.

a) Many fish are farmed outdoors in cages placed in open-water (e.g. lakes, the sea).
Some fish are farmed indoors in tanks.
Suggest **two** advantages of farming fish in indoor tanks over farming fish in open-water.

1. ....

....

2. ....

....

[2]

b) Farmed fish may be selectively bred so that each fish gives a higher protein yield.
Describe a method that fish farmers could use to do this.

....

....

....

....

[3]

[Total 5 marks]

Exam Practice Tip

In an exam, you might get asked to describe a method for growing orchids via plant tissue culture (or something similar). If so, make sure you tailor your description to the context given in the question — i.e. in this example, you must write about orchids in your answer and not just plants in general.

Score:

16

Section 9 — Use of Biological Resources

Mixed Questions for Paper 1

1   Shwachman-Diamond syndrome (SDS) is a disease that can cause neutropenia. Neutropenia is a reduction in the number of neutrophils in the blood. Neutrophils are a type of phagocyte.

a) i) People with SDS who have neutropenia are at a higher risk of infection. Explain why.

....

....

....

[2]

ii) Neutropenia can be diagnosed by looking at a patient's absolute neutrophil count (ANC). This is the number of neutrophils present in a blood sample.

The table on the right shows the ANC ranges used in the diagnosis of neutropenia. Give the diagnosis for a patient with an ANC of 1.2×10^6 / cm^3.

ANC / mm^3	Diagnosis
1000–1500	mild neutropenia
500–1000	moderate neutropenia
< 500	severe neutropenia

Diagnosis: ....

[1]

b) SNS can also damage the pancreas, leading to problems with digestion. This may result in people with SNS having problems with their bones and teeth. Suggest why.

....

....

....

[2]

[Total 5 marks]

2   Gujarat is a state in India. Most of its national parks contain a large variety of different species and are popular with tourists. The diagram shows a food web containing a number of different organisms that live in one national park.

a) How many secondary consumers are shown in the diagram?

☐ **A** 2

☐ **B** 3

☐ **C** 4

☐ **D** 5

[1]

b) When a chital deer sees an Asiatic lion running towards it, the deer responds by running away.
These events lead to an increase in the deer's heart rate.
Explain how the deer seeing the approaching lion and the deer running away each results
in an increase in the deer's heart rate.

....

....

....

....

....

....

....

....

....

[6]

c) Using your knowledge of energy transfer, explain why the number of Asiatic lions
will always be lower than the number of chital deer in this ecosystem.

....

....

....

....

....

[4]

d) *Chloris barbata* is a type of plant found in Gujarat. An environmental scientist wanted to
estimate the population size of *Chloris barbata* in an area of one national park.
Describe a method that the scientist could have used.

....

....

....

....

....

[4]

[Total 15 marks]

Exam Practice Tip

Don't be thrown by standard form — it just makes numbers with lots of zeros more manageable.
The power of 10 given is the number of places the decimal point moves. If it's positive, the point
moves right and if it's negative, it moves left. E.g. 3.4×10^3 is 3400 and 3.4×10^{-3} is 0.0034.

Score:

20

More Mixed Questions for Paper 1

1   The photos below show two different hares. The hare on the left lives in a very cold climate. The hare on the right lives in a warm climate.

The hare on the right uses its large ears as a cooling mechanism. They allow lots of heat to leave the hare's body and regulate its temperature. The hare on the left has smaller ears.

a) Suggest how the species of hare on the left evolved to have smaller ears than hares that live in warmer climates.

....

....

....

....

....

....

....

....

[5]

b) The ears of the hare on the right contain lots of blood vessels.
Suggest how these blood vessels help to keep the hare cool.

....

....

....

....

[2]

c) Hares curl up in cold weather.
Suggest how this helps them to maintain their body temperature.

....

....

....

....

[2]

[Total 9 marks]

2 The placenta plays an important role in pregnancy.

Blood from both the mother and the fetus flows through the placenta, but the two blood supplies do not mix. The diagram below shows the basic structure of part of the placenta.

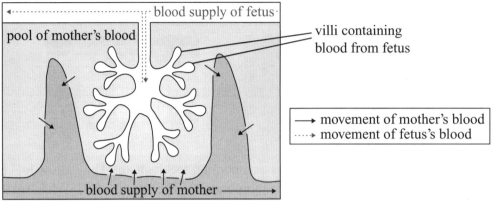

a) Using the information in the diagram, describe **one** way in which the placenta is adapted for the exchange of substances.

....

....

[1]

b) The rate of blood flow to the placenta from the mother increases during pregnancy.
Towards the end of pregnancy, approximately 39 dm³ of blood is supplied to the placenta from the mother every hour. Calculate the rate of blood flow to the placenta in cm³ per second.

blood flow = ... cm³ per second

[2]

c) Placental insufficiency can occur if the placenta does not develop properly.
This condition can result in the blood supply from the mother to the placenta not increasing as much as it should during pregnancy.

i) Placental insufficiency can result in fetal growth restriction. This is where the fetus develops at a slower rate than expected during pregnancy. Suggest why this occurs.

....

....

[1]

ii) One method of treating fetal growth restriction is by using drugs which result in vasodilation of the blood vessels from the mother to the placenta. Suggest why these drugs are used.

....

....

[1]

[Total 5 marks]

Score:

14

Mixed Questions for Paper 2

1   Read the passage below, then answer the questions that follow.

Coast redwoods

1   Coast redwoods, found on the Pacific coast, are the tallest trees in the world and have been
     known to reach heights of around 100 m. They are one of the oldest living organisms on the
     planet, and their life span can stretch to more than 2000 years. Their elaborate root systems
     extend out 30 m from the trunk and intertwine with those of neighbouring trees, allowing them
5   to share nutrients. Their seedlings need high soil moisture as they lack root hairs. Redwood
     forests absorb more carbon dioxide than any other forest on the planet, meaning that they also
     have an important role to play in alleviating one of the effects of global deforestation.

     A condition known as albinism can affect coast redwoods. A rare mutation causes unusual
     shoots to grow from and remain attached to the roots of a parent tree. The leaves of these shoots
10   lack chlorophyll, which is usually produced by an enzyme. They therefore appear white and
     survive by obtaining sugars from their host redwood trees. Despite not producing chlorophyll,
     albino redwoods display positive phototropism.

     Scientists have analysed the needles of albino redwoods. They found that they contain more
     than twice the concentration of toxic metal ions, including nickel, than the needles of the parent
15   plant to which they are attached. They also found that albino leaves have defective stomata,
     which cannot close properly.

     It has been suggested that a relationship exists between the parent plant and the mutant growths,
     whereby each provides a benefit to the other. However, it is currently unclear what the albino
     growths provide in return for obtaining sugars from the parent plant. It is also unclear why there
20   are so few albino redwoods.

     Many people are eager to see these albino plants for themselves. Some plant breeders would
     like to sell albino redwood plants, especially around Christmas time. Micropropagation is a
     method that is being explored as a way to obtain more albino redwoods. But, in the meantime,
     every effort is being made to keep their exact locations a secret.

a) Explain why not having root hairs means that redwood seedlings
     require high soil moisture (line 5).

     ....

     ....

     ....

[2]

b) Explain why the ability of redwood forest to absorb carbon dioxide is so important (lines 6-7).

....

....

....
[2]

c) Explain how a mutation could result in a lack of chlorophyll in albino redwoods (lines 9-10).

....

....

....
[3]

d) Albino redwoods display positive phototropism, even though they don't
   produce chlorophyll (lines 11-12). Explain how they achieve this response.

....

....

....
[3]

e) There is a higher concentration of nickel ions in albino redwood needles
   than in the needles of the parent plants (lines 14-15).

   i) Suggest how the albino redwoods' defective stomata (lines 15-16)
      may contribute to nickel ions building up in their needles.

   ....

   ....

   ....
   [2]

   ii) Suggest how the accumulation of nickel ions by the albino redwood may benefit the parent plant.

   ....

   ....
   [1]

f) Suggest and explain **one** difficulty with using micropropagation
   to grow albino redwood trees (lines 22-23).

....

....

....
[2]

[Total 15 marks]

Score:

15

More Mixed Questions for Paper 2

1 For millions of years a marsupial called the thylacine lived throughout mainland Australia. However, about 3000 years ago, they became extinct on the mainland and only existed on the smaller Australian island of Tasmania. When the British arrived there in 1803, there were around 3000 individuals, but hunting led to the complete extinction of the species. The dingo was probably brought to mainland Australia around 4000 years ago by sea traders from Asia. It is similar to the thylacine in that it has a comparable body mass and diet. The thylacine population rapidly declined after dingoes were first brought to Australia.

Thylacine

Dingo

a) Suggest **two** reasons to explain why the thylacine population rapidly declined in mainland Australia after the arrival of dingoes.

1. ....

2. ....

[2]

b) The last thylacine died in 1936. Calculate the average rate of decline of thylacines in Tasmania between British settlement and their extinction.

.................thylacines per year

[2]

Scientists have so far been unable to extract a nucleus from biological material preserved from a thylacine. However, if they could in the future, it may be possible to bring back thylacines through animal cloning, using a related species such as the Tasmanian devil.

c) Describe how animal cloning could potentially be used to re-establish the thylacine species.

....

....

....

....

....

....

....

....

....

[6]

[Total 10 marks]

2 Human interactions with ecosystems can change the abiotic conditions, reducing biodiversity.

a) Explain how the application of mineral fertilisers on farmland
may reduce the biodiversity of nearby water sources.

....

....

....

....

....

....

....

....

[6]

b) Fish can be farmed in nets in the ocean. However, this method of fish farming can cause
similar problems to excess fertilisers in surrounding waters. Suggest an explanation for this.

....

....

....

[2]

c) Human activity produces lots of sulfur dioxide. Suggest and explain **one** way in
which sulfur dioxide emissions may lead to a reduction in biodiversity.

....

....

....

[2]

[Total 10 marks]

3 Many human hormones can now be produced artificially.
This has helped to treat a range of conditions.

a) Insulin is needed to treat Type 1 diabetes (a condition where the body does not produce insulin).
Describe how genetic engineering may be used to produce a population of bacteria that secrete
human insulin.

....

....

....

....

....

[4]

b) FSH is an important female sex hormone.
Synthetic FSH can be taken by women with a low level of FSH in their blood.

   i) State where in the body FSH is normally produced.

....

[1]

   ii) Suggest why a low level of FSH in the blood may prevent a woman from getting pregnant.

....

....

....

[2]

   iii) Men also produce FSH. A low FSH level in men can lead to a low testosterone level.
Suggest **one** reason why men with a low testosterone level may have difficulty conceiving a child.

....

....

[1]

[Total 8 marks]

4   Herbicides are chemicals that are used to kill plants.

a) Some herbicides stop a plant's growth by either disrupting mitosis in the plant's stem cells,
or by interfering with DNA replication prior to mitosis.
Suggest **one** way in which herbicides may disrupt mitosis and prevent a plant's growth:

....

....

[1]

b) Dinitroanilines are herbicides that prevent plant stem cells from multiplying, but still
allow them to differentiate. Bipyridiliums are herbicides that destroy cell membranes.

Explain why plants treated with dinitroanilines may survive
longer than those treated with bipyridiliums.

....

....

....

....

....

[4]

[Total 5 marks]

Score:

33

Answers

Section 1 — The Nature and Variety of Living Organisms

Pages 1-4 — Cells and Transport

1 a) Similarity: e.g. both have a cytoplasm/cell membrane/cell wall *[1 mark]*. Difference: e.g. only *Symbiodinium* has a nucleus/chloroplasts *[1 mark]*.

b) i) Experiment 1 was included in the study as a control *[1 mark]*. This showed that in the absence of bacteria, the quantum yield/photosynthetic efficiency of *Symbiodinium* remained relatively constant *[1 mark]*.

ii) In Experiment 2, the bacteria infect and kill the *Symbiodinium*, causing their quantum yield/photosynthetic efficiency to decrease over time *[1 mark]*. In Experiment 3, the bacteriophage kills the bacteria, so the *Symbiodinium* survive and their quantum yield/photosynthetic efficiency is unaffected *[1 mark]*.

c) Any one from: e.g. they cannot respire/respond to their surroundings/control their internal conditions/excrete waste/grow/develop. / They don't need nutrition. / They can only move/reproduce inside living cells. *[1 mark]*

Bacteriophages are viruses not living cells. They don't share the eight characteristics that all living organisms do.

2 In both types of cell, water molecules would have moved into the cells via osmosis *[1 mark]* because the sugar concentration in the beakers was lower than it was in the cells / because the sugar solution in the beakers had a higher water concentration than the cells *[1 mark]*. The animal cells may have become so swollen that they burst, whereas the plant cells had cell walls to support/strengthen them, which may have prevented them from bursting *[1 mark]*.

3 a) i) differentiation *[1 mark]*

ii) E.g. ribosomes *[1 mark]*

Remember, ribosomes are where proteins are made in a cell.

b) HSCs are unlikely to be able to differentiate into all specialised cell types, such as beta cells *[1 mark]*.

Stem cells found in adults are not able to form all specialised cell types.

c) E.g. using modified adult stem cells does not involve the use/destruction of embryos *[1 mark]*, which some people may object to for ethical/religious reasons *[1 mark]*.

4 a) E.g. the student could have used the scalpel to cut the agar into cubes of different sizes *[1 mark]*. She could have then placed one agar cube into a beaker filled with enough dilute hydrochloric acid to cover the cube *[1 mark]*. She should have then timed how long it took for the cube to become completely colourless *[1 mark]*. She should have repeated this at least three times, using a different agar cube of the same size each time, and calculated a mean result *[1 mark]*. She should have repeated the whole experiment with the different sized cubes and compared the results *[1 mark]*. She should have made sure that the experiments were carried out at the same temperature / that the same concentration of hydrochloric acid was used / that she started recording the time at the same point after adding the cube to the beaker *[1 mark]*.

b) Any two from: e.g. the agar cubes were not the same shape as bacterial cells *[1 mark]*. / The agar cubes were bigger than bacterial cells *[1 mark]*. / Exchange of substances across the outer surface of a bacterial cell may involve active transport as well as diffusion *[1 mark]*. / The agar cubes did not have a cell membrane *[1 mark]*.

c) Cell A, because it has a bigger surface area to volume ratio than cell B *[1 mark]*. This means it will be able to absorb the substances it needs for metabolic reactions more quickly than cell B, so it will have a faster metabolic rate *[1 mark]*.

5 a) E.g. 20.0 cm = 200 mm *[1 mark]*
$200 \div 79 = 2.531... =$ **2.5 mm per second** (to 2 s.f.) *[1 mark]*

b) 3 drops *[1 mark]*

c) Increasing the concentration of ammonia increases the rate of diffusion *[1 mark]*.

d) E.g. the volume of the ammonia drops *[1 mark]*, which could have been controlled by measuring them with a dropping pipette *[1 mark]*. / The size of the litmus paper *[1 mark]*, which could have been controlled by measuring the length and width of the strip with a ruler *[1 mark]*. / The distance the ammonia had to travel *[1 mark]*, which could have been controlled by making sure the distance between the cotton wool and litmus paper was the same each time *[1 mark]*.

Page 5 — Enzymes

1 a) i) E.g.

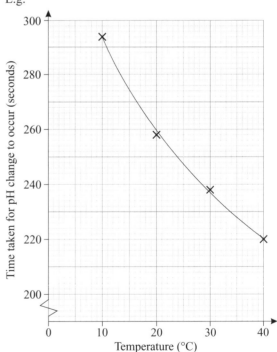

[4 marks — 1 mark for a correct scale and labels on the y-axis, 1 mark for a correct scale and labels on the x-axis, 1 mark for all 4 data points correctly plotted, 1 mark for a smooth curve of best fit that passes through or as near to as many points as possible.]

ii) 228 seconds *[1 mark]*

Your curve of best fit may differ slightly so accept any answer between 226 and 230 seconds, as long as the answer has been read correctly from the curve of best fit.

b) E.g. the time taken for the pH to change will increase / there will be no pH change *[1 mark]*. This is because if the temperature gets too high, some of the bonds holding the enzyme together break, which changes the shape of the enzyme's active site *[1 mark]*. The enzyme becomes denatured and can no longer catalyse the reaction *[1 mark]*.

Section 2 — Human Nutrition

Pages 6-8 — Human Nutrition

1 a) E.g. add a few drops of Sudan III stain solution to a test tube containing the food sample and shake gently *[1 mark]*. If fats are present, a red layer will form on top *[1 mark]*.

b) By flattening the villi, tropical sprue reduces the surface area of the small intestine *[1 mark]*. This means that fewer products from the digestion of fat/fatty acids and glycerol molecules would be absorbed into blood *[1 mark]*.

c) i) Pancreatitis may cause less lipase to be secreted from the pancreas *[1 mark]*, meaning that less fat is digested/ broken down (into fatty acids and glycerol) *[1 mark]*. Therefore, more fat will pass through the body and be present in the faeces *[1 mark]*.

ii) The enzymes may be denatured when exposed to a high temperature *[1 mark]*.

iii) An obstruction in the tubes leading from the gallbladder could mean that less bile reaches the small intestine *[1 mark]*. This would mean that fats are not emulsified/ broken down into tiny droplets as quickly *[1 mark]*, reducing the rate at which fat is digested and absorbed *[1 mark]*. This could lead to the person obtaining less energy from their food, which may lead to weight loss *[1 mark]*.

2 a) To obtain the additional energy she needs to run the marathon *[1 mark]*.

b) He has a decreased surface area for absorption of nutrients/less villi *[1 mark]*, so fewer amino acids can be absorbed/are available to build muscle *[1 mark]*. Fewer enzymes will also be produced, so the rate of digestion of large molecules to form smaller molecules, e.g. proteins into amino acids, will decrease *[1 mark]*, so fewer amino acids will be available to build muscles *[1 mark]*.

c) $(3450 - 2500) \div 2500 = 0.38 \times 100 = \textbf{38\%}$
[2 marks for the correct answer, otherwise 1 mark for the correct calculation]

3 D *[1 mark]*

4 a) E.g. break up a set mass of each food, dissolve it in a set volume of distilled water and filter the solutions *[1 mark]*. Heat each solution up to 75 °C and add Benedict's solution *[1 mark]*. If the solution remains blue, no glucose is present *[1 mark]*. If the colour of the solution changes to yellow, green or brick-red, it indicates that glucose is present, with a brick-red colour indicating a higher concentration of glucose than a yellow/green solution *[1 mark]*.

b) E.g. measure the mass of a marshmallow and the mass of a crisp in grams/g *[1 mark]*. Set fire to each food and use it to heat a set volume of water in a boiling tube *[1 mark]*. Burn the food under the boiling tube until the food no longer relights *[1 mark]*. Measure and record the temperature change of the water *[1 mark]*. Use the temperature change of the water to calculate the energy of each food sample in joules/J *[1 mark]*.

c) $2436 \div 0.20 = 12\ 180$
$2400 \div 0.24 = 10\ 000$
$12\ 180 - 10\ 000 = \textbf{2180 J/g}$
[2 marks for the correct answer, otherwise 1 mark for dividing the energy of each food by the mass of that food in g]

d) Any two from: e.g. ensure each food sample is used to heat the same volume of water / hold the burning food samples the same distance away from the boiling tubes / keep the temperature of the environment the same for each food sample / use the same degree of insulation for each boiling tube.
[2 marks — 1 mark for each correct answer].

Section 3 — Plant Nutrition and Transport

Pages 9-10 — Plant Nutrition and Transport

1 a) In order for a plant to increase in mass it also needs carbon dioxide, light and mineral ions *[1 mark]*.

b) i) Percentage change in mass for Location C =
$\dfrac{44.4 - 2.0}{2.0} \times 100 = 2120.0\%$
Mean percentage change in mass =
$(957.1 + 1876.5 + 2120.0) \div 3 = \textbf{1651.2\%}$
[3 marks for correct answer, otherwise 1 mark for correct working to calculate percentage change, and 1 mark for correctly calculating percentage change]

ii) Any two from: e.g. the amount of water given to each tree. / The type of tree grown. / The size of the pot the tree was grown in. / The type of soil used. / The position of the tree outside (e.g. how exposed to sunlight it was) *[2 marks]*.

iii) E.g. Location B might have had higher average temperatures / more hours of sunlight than Location A *[1 mark]*. This would mean the tree planted at Location B would have had a higher rate of photosynthesis, leading to a greater increase in mass *[1 mark]*.

2 a) Distance: 20 cm *[1 mark]*.
Explanation: the readings at this distance have the lowest range/are all close to the mean *[1 mark]*.

b) Above a certain light intensity, the rate of photosynthesis won't increase further because the carbon dioxide concentration or temperature will become the limiting factor (hence a similar volume of gas is produced at both 5 cm and 10 cm) *[1 mark]*.

c) Type of bulb: LED *[1 mark]*.
Explanation: The change in temperature as the lamp moves further from the pondweed affects the rate of photosynthesis, so would affect the volume of gas given off by the plant/the results of the experiment *[1 mark]*. Using the LED bulb would have the least effect, as it operates at the lowest temperature *[1 mark]*.

Pages 11-13 — More Plant Nutrition and Transport

1 a) Keeping the plant in the dark for a few days meant that the plant used up its starch stores *[1 mark]*. This proved that any starch present in the leaf at the end of the experiment was produced during the experiment (and not before it) *[1 mark]*. This helped to make the experiment a fair test, increasing the validity of the results *[1 mark]*.

b) The black strip of paper stops sunlight from reaching the leaf *[1 mark]*.

c) Boiling the leaf in water stops any further chemical reactions from taking place inside the leaf *[1 mark]*. Boiling the leaf in alcohol removes the chlorophyll from the leaf *[1 mark]*.

d) The leaf would have turned blue-black in all areas apart from that covered by the black strip of paper (which would have turned brown) *[1 mark]*. The parts of the leaf that weren't covered by the paper were exposed to light, so they could photosynthesise and produce starch *[1 mark]*. The area covered by the paper was not exposed to light, so could not photosynthesise or produce starch *[1 mark]*.

2 a) *Pythium* destroys root hair cells and therefore decreases the surface area available for the absorption of water from the soil *[1 mark]*. This will mean that less water will be available to be drawn up from the roots by the transpiration stream *[1 mark]*.

b) E.g. if the root hair cells are destroyed, a plant will have difficulty absorbing mineral ions from the soil *[1 mark]*. / The disruption to the transpiration stream will reduce the plant's ability to transport mineral ions from the roots to where they're needed in the plant *[1 mark]*.

3 a) E.g.

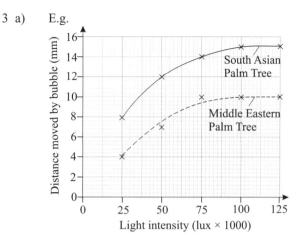

[6 marks — 2 marks for all 10 points correctly plotted (or 1 mark for 8 or 9 points correctly plotted), 1 mark for a suitable scale and label on the x-axis, 1 mark for a suitable scale and label on the y-axis, 1 mark for two smooth curves of best fit, 1 mark for correctly labelled curves.]

b) It made the experiment valid / enabled a fair comparison *[1 mark]*. This is because plants lose water vapour from the stomata in leaves *[1 mark]*, so if one tree had a higher surface area of leaves, it may have lost water more quickly *[1 mark]*.

c) E.g. repeat the experiment several times at each light intensity and calculate a mean *[1 mark]*. / Repeat the experiment using another pair of palm tree saplings to see if the same results are obtained *[1 mark]*.

d) Both palm trees lose more water by transpiration as light intensity increases *[1 mark]*. This is because as light intensity increases, more stomata open to maximise the rate of photosynthesis and water vapour escapes *[1 mark]*. Both palm trees have a transpiration rate that reaches a plateau at high light intensities *[1 mark]*. This is because at high light intensities all stomata are fully open, so the rate of transpiration can't increase further *[1 mark]*. The Middle Eastern palm tree has a lower transpiration rate than the South Asian palm tree at all light intensities *[1 mark]*. This may be because the Middle Eastern palm lives in an environment where humidity is low, so it might have fewer stomata/adaptations to minimise water loss by transpiration *[1 mark]*.
[Accept reverse reasoning for South Asian palm tree having a higher transpiration rate.]

If the air is not very humid it means there's not a lot of water in it. This means there's likely to be a bigger water concentration gradient between the inside and the outside of the leaf, so water will diffuse out of the leaves more quickly.

Section 4 — Respiration and Gas Exchange

Pages 14-16 — Respiration and Gas Exchange

1 a) A change in the shape of the alveoli may reduce their surface area, reducing gas exchange *[1 mark]*. Inflammation and narrowing of the bronchi restricts the airflow into the lungs, reducing the concentration gradient for gas exchange *[1 mark]*.

b) i) Patient A:
2.5 hours = 2.5 × 60 = 150 minutes.
$2250 \div 150 = $ **15 breaths per minute** *[1 mark]*
Patient B:
$750 \div 30 = $ **25 breaths per minute** *[1 mark]*

   ii) Patient: B
Explanation: their breathing rate is higher to compensate for the reduced gas exchange they are experiencing, due to the changes in the lungs *[1 mark]*.

c) i) People with AATD have low levels of AAT, which means the alveoli could become damaged by the enzymes produced by the white blood cells *[1 mark]*. This could result in the alveoli changing shape, leading to emphysema/COPD *[1 mark]*.

   ii) Cigarette smoke causes the white blood cells to produce more of the enzymes that may damage the lung cell proteins *[1 mark]*. The more a person smokes, the more enzymes will be produced, increasing the risk of damage to cells in their lungs, which can lead to emphysema/COPD *[1 mark]*.

2 a) i) It increases the volume of the thorax *[1 mark]*, which reduces the pressure so that air is drawn into the lungs *[1 mark]*.

   ii) E.g. that other muscles are also used for breathing *[1 mark]*.

b) E.g. the stiff rings of cartilage prevent the trachea from collapsing / keep the trachea open *[1 mark]* when the pressure in the lungs/thorax drops *[1 mark]*.

c) pleural membranes *[1 mark]*

3 a) Oxygen consumption increased rapidly at first then increased more slowly *[1 mark]*, until around 8 minutes when it levelled off *[1 mark]*.

b) A *[1 mark]*

You should have learnt the balanced symbol equation for aerobic respiration: $C_6H_{12}O_6 + 6O_2 \rightarrow 6CO_2 + 6H_2O$. This shows that it takes 6 O_2 molecules to produce 6 CO_2 molecules — so for every 1 molecule of O_2 consumed, 1 molecule of CO_2 is produced.

c) i) Aerobic respiration produces more ATP molecules per molecule of glucose than anaerobic respiration *[1 mark]*.

   ii) In the final two minutes of exercise, the volunteer's oxygen consumption remained constant *[1 mark]*. This suggests that his muscles were respiring anaerobically to supply the extra energy needed for his muscles to continue to work harder, as this process doesn't require oxygen *[1 mark]*.

Pages 17-18 — More Respiration and Gas Exchange

1 a) i) E.g. the indicator would have turned purple *[1 mark]* as the concentration of carbon dioxide in both test tubes would have decreased *[1 mark]*. This is because the amount of carbon dioxide taken in by each leaf for photosynthesis would have exceeded the amount of carbon dioxide released by respiration *[1 mark]*.

   ii) Test tube 1. This is because the leaf from plant 1 has a greater stomatal density than the leaf from plant 2 *[1 mark]*. The rate of gas exchange in the leaf from plant 1 will therefore be faster *[1 mark]*, which means that carbon dioxide will be removed from the air in the test tube more quickly *[1 mark]*.

b) Any two from: e.g. the temperature at which the experiment was carried out / the species of the plant the leaves were taken from / the age of the leaves / the time between removing the leaves from the plants and carrying out the experiment / the health of the leaves *[2 marks]*.

c) E.g. the plants may grow more leaves/broader leaves *[1 mark]* as this would increase the surface area for carbon dioxide to diffuse into the leaf *[1 mark]*.

d) That the carbon dioxide concentration at the time the plants were alive was lower than it is today *[1 mark]*.

2 a) Oxygen consumption is lower at night (12 am) because organism A is asleep *[1 mark]* and higher during the day (12 pm) because organism A is awake and active *[1 mark]*. The more active the organism is, the more energy it will need to transfer through respiration, therefore it will need to consume more oxygen *[1 mark]*.

b) Between 7 am and 12 pm, the mean net oxygen consumption is below zero and continues to fall *[1 mark]*. This means that organism B is producing more oxygen through photosynthesis than it is using up through aerobic respiration *[1 mark]*.

Section 5 — Blood and Organs

Pages 19-22 — Blood and Organs

1 a) E.g. 1991 ÷ 5.5 = 362 cm^3/min
362 × 60 = 21 720 cm^3/hour
21 720 × 24 = **521 280 cm^3/day** *[2 marks for correct answer, otherwise 1 mark for correct working]*

b) A lack of haemoglobin means that less oxygen can be transported around the body *[1 mark]*. This means the body cells don't have as much oxygen available for (aerobic) respiration *[1 mark]*, meaning they transfer less energy, so the person feels tired and weak *[1 mark]*.

c) If lymphocytes are not activated, fewer antibodies will be produced in response to a pathogen *[1 mark]*. This will prevent the pathogen being marked for destruction/destroyed by other white blood cells *[1 mark]*, allowing it to multiply and cause disease *[1 mark]*.

d) If Factor V is deficient, not as much prothrombin can be converted into thrombin, which may lead to fewer platelets being activated *[1 mark]*. Having fewer active platelets may mean that the blood can't clot as well as it should *[1 mark]*, so a person may be at risk of excessive bleeding during/after surgery *[1 mark]*.

2 a) C *[1 mark]*

b) i) E.g. an elite athlete's heart has to regularly pump more blood around the body than a non-athlete's heart, in order to provide the muscles with enough oxygen when exercising *[1 mark]*. The left ventricle is responsible for pumping blood around the body *[1 mark]*. A larger chamber size and thicker wall allow it to pump a larger volume of blood with each heartbeat / withstand the pressure created by a larger volume of blood *[1 mark]*.

ii) During the race, the athlete's respiration rate increases, which increases the level of carbon dioxide in the blood *[1 mark]*. A high level of carbon dioxide in the blood is detected by receptors in the athlete's aorta/carotid artery *[1 mark]*. These receptors send impulses to the athlete's brain, which sends impulses to the athlete's heart, causing it to contract more frequently *[1 mark]*.

3 a) Blood flow through the bicuspid valve will be reduced, so blood flow out of the left atrium will be reduced *[1 mark]*. This will cause the volume of blood (and pressure) in the left atrium to increase, which could cause the left atrium to get bigger *[1 mark]*.

b) Any two from: e.g. Factor: smoking. Explanation: it leads to high blood pressure, which can damage the coronary arteries and make it more likely that fatty deposits will form, reducing blood flow to the heart muscle. / Factor: a diet high in saturated fat. Explanation: it can lead to fatty deposits forming inside the coronary arteries, which narrows the arteries and reduces blood flow to the heart muscle. / Factor: being inactive. Explanation: it leads to high blood pressure, which can damage the coronary arteries and make it more likely that fatty deposits will form, reducing blood flow to the heart muscle.
[1 mark for correct factor, plus 1 mark for the correct corresponding explanation, up to a maximum of 4 marks]

4 E.g. the vaccine will contain antigens found on the meningococcal B bacteria (e.g. it may contain small amounts of dead or inactive meningococcal B bacteria) *[1 mark]*. When the vaccine is injected into the baby's bloodstream, the antigens will cause the baby's lymphocytes to produce antibodies against meningococcal B bacteria *[1 mark]*. The immune system will also produce memory cells, which are able to recognise the meningococcal B bacteria's antigens and remain in the bloodstream *[1 mark]*. If the baby is later infected with the meningococcal B bacteria, these memory cells will be able to rapidly mass produce antibodies to attack the pathogen and will be able to get rid of it quickly, before it causes meningitis *[1 mark]*. However, the meningococcal C bacteria carries different antigens to the meningococcal B bacteria *[1 mark]*. This means that if the baby is infected with the meningococcal C bacteria, it will not have memory cells capable of recognising the antigens, so it won't be able to quickly produce the specific antibodies needed to attack the meningococcal C bacteria *[1 mark]*.

5 a) During exercise, water is lost from the body in sweat *[1 mark]*. This causes the blood water content to fall *[1 mark]*. The body responds by releasing more ADH so that more water is reabsorbed back into the blood from the kidney tubules *[1 mark]*.

b) If ADH isn't produced, water in the blood won't be reabsorbed from the kidney tubules *[1 mark]*. This means the person will have a low blood water concentration *[1 mark]*, so they may need to drink more to restore the normal water balance in the body *[1 mark]*.

6 a) Any two from: e.g. proteins and red blood cells could leak into the urine *[1 mark]*. / Waste products could build up in the blood *[1 mark]*. / Water could build up in the body *[1 mark]*.

b) E.g. 70 × 75 = 5250 cm^3 per min
20% of 5250 = 0.2 × 5250 = 1050 cm^3 per min
1050 × 60 = **63 000 cm^3 per hour**
[2 marks for correct answer, otherwise 1 mark for correct working]

Section 6 — Coordination and Response

Pages 23-25 — Coordination and Response

1 a) It reduces energy transfer from the surface of the skin to the surroundings *[1 mark]*, which helps to maintain the person's body temperature *[1 mark]*.

   b) The skin contains temperature receptors *[1 mark]*, which detect the cold temperature of the water and send nervous impulses *[1 mark]* to the brain *[1 mark]*. Based on the signals from these receptors, the central nervous system sends impulses to effectors/muscles surrounding the blood vessels that supply the skin capillaries *[1 mark]*. This causes vasoconstriction/the blood vessels to constrict, which restricts the blood flow to the surface of the skin *[1 mark]*.

2 By preventing the release of neurotransmitters, opioids prevent information being transmitted across synapses *[1 mark]* between sensory neurones and (relay) neurones in the spinal cord *[1 mark]*. This means the information about the stimulus doesn't reach the brain, so no pain is felt *[1 mark]*.

3 E.g. the student could measure and record how long it takes a volunteer to press a button when they see a shape on a computer screen *[1 mark]*. The student could then give the same volunteer a cup of coffee, wait 30 minutes, then ask the volunteer to repeat the test *[1 mark]*. The student could ask the volunteer to repeat the test three times before drinking the coffee and three times after drinking the coffee, then calculate the volunteer's mean reaction time before and after drinking the coffee *[1 mark]*. The student could then repeat this for several different volunteers and compare the results *[1 mark]*. The student should make sure the same volume/concentration/brand of coffee is drunk by each volunteer *[1 mark]*. The student should make sure all the volunteers are the same age/sex/distance from the computer screen *[1 mark]*.

4 a) Light receptors in the retina detect bright light *[1 mark]*. These receptors send nervous impulses along a sensory neurone to the central nervous system *[1 mark]*. In the CNS, the sensory neurone passes the impulse to a relay neurone *[1 mark]*, which then passes the impulse to a motor neurone *[1 mark]*. The impulse then travels along the motor neurone to the effector(s) / circular muscles in the iris *[1 mark]*. This causes the circular muscles in the iris to contract, making the pupil smaller *[1 mark]*.

   b) Yes, because the nervous impulses involved in this reflex response do not pass through the conscious part of the brain *[1 mark]*.

   c) E.g. nervous responses are faster than hormonal responses *[1 mark]*, which means the iris can contract quickly to prevent bright light damaging the eye *[1 mark]*.

5 a) The ciliary muscles don't relax, so the suspensory ligaments remain loose *[1 mark]*. This means that the lens remains thick/round *[1 mark]*, so light from distant objects will not be focused on the retina (and will appear blurry/unclear) *[1 mark]*.

   b) Reshaping the cornea will change the angle at which light is bent/refracted into the eye *[1 mark]*, so light rays will focus on the retina (rather than in front of it or behind it) *[1 mark]*.

Page 26 — Plant Coordination and Response

1 a) Plant roots are positively geotropic / grow towards gravity *[1 mark]*.

   b) Because light can affect the direction of root growth / plant roots are phototrophic *[1 mark]*, so altering the intensity or direction of the light could have altered the results *[1 mark]*.

   c) A *[1 mark]*

   d) Continuous rotation of the clinostat prevented the roots from growing towards gravity *[1 mark]*.

Section 7 — Reproduction and Inheritance

Pages 27-28 — Reproduction

1 a) i) Any two from: e.g. no liquid water / low temperature / low oxygen concentration *[1 mark for each]*.

   ii) E.g. the seeds may not have had enough food reserves to sustain them until the plants were able to start photosynthesising *[1 mark]*.

   b) E.g. cloning plants from fruit tissue produces genetically identical offspring, whereas growing them from seed produces genetically varied offspring *[1 mark]*.

   c) i) A *[1 mark]*

   ii) A *[1 mark]*

2 a) 21 days *[1 mark]*

   b) The level of LH will be lower at point X than at point Y *[1 mark]* because high levels of progesterone inhibit LH secretion *[1 mark]*.

   c) Female A's progesterone level remains high *[1 mark]*. This is because progesterone maintains the uterus lining/ prevents menstruation (which would terminate the pregnancy) *[1 mark]*.

   d) Progesterone is produced from the remains of a follicle after ovulation *[1 mark]*. As Female C doesn't ovulate, there are no eggs released and so no follicles present, meaning her progesterone level is very low / doesn't change *[1 mark]*.

Pages 29-32 — DNA and Inheritance

1   E.g. RNA polymerase binds to non-coding DNA located in front of the insulin gene *[1 mark]*. The two DNA strands unzip and RNA polymerase moves along one of the strands, using the coding DNA in the insulin gene as a template to make mRNA *[1 mark]*. Base pairing ensures the mRNA is complementary to the insulin gene, e.g. the base A in DNA pairs with U in mRNA *[1 mark]*. The mRNA moves out of the nucleus and attaches to a ribosome in the cytoplasm of the pancreas cell *[1 mark]*. tRNA molecules transport amino acids to the ribosome — anticodons on the tRNA pair up with complementary codons in the mRNA to ensure that amino acids are brought to the ribosome in the correct order *[1 mark]*. The ribosome joins the amino acids together to make the insulin protein *[1 mark]*.

2 a)   There are three copies of chromosome 21 instead of two *[1 mark]*.

   b)   All of them *[1 mark]*, because the cells in the embryo divide by mitosis so they are genetically identical *[1 mark]*.

   c)   It could cause Klinefelter syndrome *[1 mark]* if fertilisation takes place, as the cell would fuse with an egg or sperm that already has one sex chromosome, producing offspring with three sex chromosomes *[1 mark]*. /
It could cause Turner syndrome *[1 mark]* because if the chromosomes fail to separate in meiosis then one gamete won't contain any sex chromosomes, so if fertilisation occurs with this gamete, offspring will only have one sex chromosome *[1 mark]*.

3 a)   GCU *[1 mark]*

   b) i)   E.g. a mutation at position 2 would lead to a change in the DNA base sequence / a different mRNA codon being produced *[1 mark]*. This could change the amino acid coded for at that position *[1 mark]*. This could change the final shape/activity of the protein produced, leading to a change in phenotype *[1 mark]*.

     ii)   The table shows that, e.g. proline can be encoded by either CCU or CCC / valine can be encoded by either GUU or GUG *[1 mark]*. Therefore some mutations will not change the encoded amino acid *[1 mark]*, which means the protein won't change and therefore neither will the phenotype *[1 mark]*.

4 a)   E.g. 423 ÷ 3 = 141
141 + 6 = 147 amino acids
[2 marks for correct answer, otherwise 1 mark for correct working]

Dividing the number of remaining bases in the gene by 3 gives the number of amino acids left in the chain, as each amino acid is coded for by 3 bases. Then you just need to add on the first 6 amino acids.

b) i)   Individual 7 is affected, so they must have inherited two recessive alleles from their parents (individuals 1 and 2) *[1 mark]*. However, both parents are unaffected, so they must both have one copy of the dominant allele *[1 mark]*.

     ii)   E.g. individual 3 may have the genotype AA *[1 mark]*, meaning none of his children would be affected, even if individual 4 is a carrier (Aa) *[1 mark]*. If both individuals 3 and 4 carried the recessive allele (Aa) *[1 mark]*, there is a chance that none of their children would be affected if at least one of them passed on their dominant allele every time *[1 mark]*.

5 a)   B *[1 mark]*

7.75 × 10⁵ is the same as 775 000.
0.005% of 775 000 = 38.75, which rounds up to 39.

   b)   E.g.

Genotypes of parents: Dd   DD

Genotypes of gametes: D   d   D   D

Genotypes of offspring: DD   Dd   DD   Dd

Phenotypes of offspring: no ARPKD   no ARPKD/ carrier   no ARPKD   no ARPKD/ carrier

Probability of child being born with ARPKD = **0**
[Maximum 4 marks available — 1 mark for correct genotypes of parents, 1 mark for correct genotypes of their gametes, 1 mark for correct genotypes of offspring with phenotypes correctly assigned, 1 mark for correct probability. Accept correct answers if shown using a Punnett square.]

Pages 33-34 — Evolution

1 a)   E.g. there will be no/less competition from other bacteria for nutrients/space in the new section *[1 mark]*.

   b)   The bacteria have divided and spread throughout the medium in both sections A and E because there is no antibiotic, so their growth is not restricted *[1 mark]*. However, they cannot spread into sections B or D because the antibiotic there prevents growth *[1 mark]*.

   c)   A bacterium in section A has undergone a mutation that allows it to survive in a low antibiotic concentration *[1 mark]*. This has enabled it to move into section B and start to reproduce *[1 mark]*. Its offspring inherit the mutation, so they can survive in section B too *[1 mark]*. There are no bacteria in section D because no bacteria in section E have undergone the necessary mutation *[1 mark]*.

d) E.g. bacterial growth would be faster / more/all of the plate sections would contain bacteria by the end of the experiment *[1 mark]*. This is because exposure to ionising radiation at the start of the experiment would increase the chance of mutations in the bacterial DNA *[1 mark]*, making it more likely that bacteria would acquire the necessary mutations to survive in the plate sections containing antibiotics *[1 mark]*.

2 a) The green paperclips were less likely to be found by students than the red paper clips because they were better camouflaged against the grass *[1 mark]*. This shows that individuals with the most suitable characteristics for the environment (in this case the green paperclips) are the more successful competitors and so will have a better chance of survival *[1 mark]*.

b) E.g. it does not illustrate how the individuals with the most suitable characteristics for the environment are more likely to reproduce *[1 mark]*. It does not illustrate how the number of individuals with the most suitable characteristics for the environment increase in the population over time *[1 mark]*.

Section 8 — Ecology and the Environment

Pages 35-36 — Ecosystems and Biodiversity

1 a) From the graph, *T. confusum* wins 18% of the time at 29 °C and 70% humidity.
Number of times *T. confusum* expected to win
= 18% of 18 (number of tests) = 0.18 × 18 = **3.24** (or 3.2 times to 2 s.f.)
[2 marks for correct answer, otherwise 1 mark for reading 18% from the graph]

b) *T. castaneum* because this species won 100% of the competition experiments in the hottest and most humid conditions (34 °C and 70% humidity) *[1 mark]*.

c) *T. castaneum*. E.g. the ability to fly provides more opportunities to find food / find space / escape predators *[1 mark]*.

These are the things that the beetles would compete for and that are needed for survival.

d) Pesticides used to control the beetles may be washed into nearby water and pollute these ecosystems *[1 mark]*. This may kill some of the organisms that live in the water and therefore reduce biodiversity *[1 mark]*.

2 a) E.g. the student could have set up a transect running from the sea up the beach *[1 mark]*, and then placed quadrats along the transect at regular intervals/at the distances stated in the table *[1 mark]*. She could have then recorded the percentage of the quadrat that each plant species covered *[1 mark]*. At each quadrat, she could also have measured the salt concentration of the soil *[1 mark]*.

b) There is a positive correlation between biodiversity and distance from the sea *[1 mark]*, because there are more species present as the distance increases *[1 mark]*.

c) E.g. sea couch may be able to tolerate higher concentrations of salt than other species *[1 mark]*, so it has the highest percentage cover near the sea *[1 mark]*. It may become less abundant further from the sea/ in lower concentrations of salt because other species are able to grow here *[1 mark]*, meaning it faces more competition *[1 mark]*.

d) E.g. different people may determine the percentage cover differently / there may be different plant coverage if the student hasn't sampled it in exactly the same place on the beach / it might be difficult to determine where the sea ends and the beach begins (depending on whether the tide is in/ out) *[1 mark]*.

Pages 37-38 — Energy Transfer in Ecosystems

1 a)

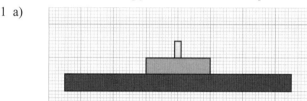

[1 mark for a bar 70 squares long and 5 squares high, 1 mark for the bar drawn in the correct position below the other two bars]

b) Biomass of primary consumer = 4 × 400 = 1600 g m^{-2}
Efficiency = (1600 ÷ 5600) × 100 = 28.571 = **29%** (2 s.f.)
[2 marks for correct answer, otherwise 1 mark for correct working]

2 If cod became extinct, zooplankton numbers might decrease *[1 mark]*. This is because crab numbers may fall as they become the main prey for seals *[1 mark]*. Shellfish numbers might then increase as there would be fewer crabs to predate on them, so more zooplankton might then be eaten by shellfish *[1 mark]*. Mullet numbers might increase, as they would no longer be eaten by cod *[1 mark]*. Whales might also eat more sea trout in the absence of cod, which means there would be fewer sea trout to predate on mullet and on shrimp *[1 mark]*. This could lead to an increase in the number of shrimp, providing more food for the mullet and increasing mullet numbers further *[1 mark]*.

3 a) $1.25 \times 10^6 = 1\,250\,000$
       $(3 \div 1\,250\,000) \times 100 = 0.00024 = \mathbf{2.4 \times 10^{-4}\%}$
       [2 marks for correct answer, otherwise 1 mark for correct working]

  b)   Primary consumers, because there is more energy available to them, so more individuals can be supported *[1 mark]*.

  c)   Most of the energy released by respiration is transferred from the organisms in the community to their surroundings by heat *[1 mark]*.

  d)   E.g. faeces and urine *[2 marks]*.

Page 39 — Carbon and Nitrogen Cycles

1 a)   E.g. when the mouse died, other animals and microorganisms may have eaten its remains, so the carbon in its body would have then become part of these organisms *[1 mark]*. When these organisms respired, the carbon would have been released into the atmosphere as carbon dioxide *[1 mark]*. Plants would have used the carbon dioxide in photosynthesis to make glucose/carbon compounds *[1 mark]*, which may have been stored in the seeds/used to make the seeds *[1 mark]*.

  b)   E.g. when the mouse dies, decomposers break down the proteins in its body *[1 mark]*. They also break down urea *[1 mark]*. This produces ammonia *[1 mark]*, which forms nitrogen-containing ammonium ions that can be taken up from the soil by the plants that produced the seeds *[1 mark]*. Nitrifying bacteria in the soil turn ammonia in decaying matter into nitrites and then into nitrates *[1 mark]*. These nitrogen-containing ions can also be taken up and used by the plants that produced the seeds *[1 mark]*.

Pages 40-41 — Pollution

1 a) i)   E.g. $(380 \div 470) \times 100 = \mathbf{80.9\%}$
         [2 marks for correct answer, otherwise 1 mark for correct working. Accept answers between 78% and 84%.]

   ii)   Any two from: e.g. methane / nitrous oxide / CFCs *[2 marks]*.

  b)   E.g. burning coal releases greenhouse gases such as carbon dioxide into the atmosphere *[1 mark]*. Therefore the closure of the coal power stations could have contributed to the steep decline in carbon dioxide and total greenhouse gas emissions between 2011 and 2016 *[1 mark]*.

  c)   The decrease in greenhouse gas emissions may help to reduce/limit global warming *[1 mark]*.

2 a)   Percentage decrease =
       ((final number – initial number) ÷ initial number) × 100
       $= ((15 - 75) \div 75) \times 100 = -80\% = \mathbf{80\%}$
       [2 marks for correct answer, otherwise 1 mark for correct working]

  b) i)   E.g. the tourist resort may have released sewage/waste water containing nitrates/phosphates into the river *[1 mark]*. This would have provided extra nutrients for increased algal growth *[1 mark]*.

   ii)   The algae block out the light, which means that plants in the river can't photosynthesise and die *[1 mark]*. Microorganisms that decompose the dead plants use up oxygen in the water as they respire *[1 mark]*. So the freshwater shrimp and stonefly nymph, which require a high oxygen level, decrease in number between sites 2 and 3 *[1 mark]*.

Section 9 — Use of Biological Resources

Pages 42-44 — Use of Biological Resources

1 a)   E.g. so that the plants will grow faster *[1 mark]* and the crop yield will increase *[1 mark]*.

  b)   E.g.

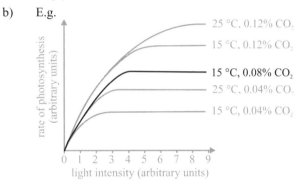

   [1 mark for drawing a line that increases at a faster rate than for 0.04% CO_2 but at a slower rate than for 0.12% CO_2, and that plateaus at a higher light intensity than for 0.04% CO_2 but at a lower light intensity than for 0.12% CO_2]

  c)   Option: C *[1 mark]*. Explanation: e.g. increasing the light intensity to 8 arbitrary units would not be beneficial as temperature and carbon dioxide concentration are limiting factors at the current light intensity of 3.2 arbitrary units *[1 mark]*. Increasing the temperature to 25 °C would increase the rate of photosynthesis, but not as much as increasing the carbon dioxide concentration to 0.12% *[1 mark]*.

  d)   At the current light intensity, increasing the carbon dioxide concentration to 0.12% would result in the same rate of photosynthesis whether the temperature was 15 °C or 25 °C *[1 mark]*. Therefore, it would be a waste of money for the farmer to increase the temperature to 25 °C *[1 mark]*.

2 a) Dough rises when pockets of carbon dioxide gas in the dough expand *[1 mark]*. The carbon dioxide is released by respiring yeast, so if no yeast are present, there will be no carbon dioxide trapped in the dough and it will not rise *[1 mark]*.

b) Any two from: e.g. the yeast might be dead / the temperature of the dough/room may be too hot/too cold for enzymes in the yeast to work effectively / the pH of the dough may be too low/high for the enzymes in the yeast to work effectively *[1 mark for each]*.

3 a) Any six from: e.g. the student could add a set volume of milk to a beaker *[1 mark]* and heat it to a set temperature using a water bath *[1 mark]*. The student could then add a set mass of bacteria to the milk *[1 mark]* and time how long it takes for yoghurt to form / the pH to drop to a particular point *[1 mark]*. The student could repeat these steps at the same temperature and calculate a mean *[1 mark]*. The student could then repeat the whole experiment at a range of different temperatures *[1 mark]*. For each repeat, the student should keep the volume/type/age of milk / the mass/strain of bacteria the same *[1 mark]*. *[Maximum of 6 marks available]*

b) E.g.

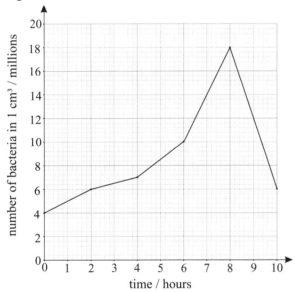

[4 marks — 1 mark for a suitable scale and label on the x-axis, 1 mark for a suitable scale and label on the y-axis, 1 mark for all 6 points correctly plotted, 1 mark for straight lines joining each of the points]

c) i) E.g. the bacteria no longer have enough nutrients/lactose to sustain them in such large numbers, so they die off. / The temperature is now too high/the pH is too high/low, which has denatured bacterial enzymes and caused the bacteria to die off. / The yoghurt has become contaminated and the bacteria are being out-competed by other organisms (e.g. fungi). *[1 mark]*.

ii) E.g. use a larger volume of milk/mass of lactose / keep temperature at the optimum level by cooling the fermenter with a water-cooled jacket / keep pH at the optimum level using a pH buffer / sterilise the vessel to ensure aseptic conditions *[1 mark]*.

Pages 45-46 — More on the Use of Biological Resources

1 a) i) B *[1 mark]*

ii) The gene is cut out using a restriction enzyme *[1 mark]*.

iii) E.g. they are both used to transfer DNA into a cell *[1 mark]*. The plasmid transfers the *Bt* toxin gene into *Agrobacterium tumefaciens* and *Agrobacterium tumefaciens* transfers the *Bt* toxin gene into the corn plant *[1 mark]*.

b) Only bacteria which have taken up the plasmid containing the antibiotic resistance gene will be able to grow on the antibiotic-containing growth medium *[1 mark]*. This means that only bacteria containing the plasmid (and therefore the *Bt* gene) are able to multiply/selected for *[1 mark]*.

c) i) E.g. plants produced via tissue culture are clones/genetically identical, so would have all inherited the *Bt* toxin gene *[1 mark]*.

ii) E.g. small pieces/explants of a *Bt* corn plant are taken from the tips of the plant's stems and side shoots *[1 mark]*. The small pieces/explants of *Bt* corn plant are sterilised and grown *in vitro* *[1 mark]* on a nutrient medium *[1 mark]*. Cells in the small pieces/explants of *Bt* corn plant divide and grow into *Bt* corn plants *[1 mark]*.

2 a) Any two from: e.g. the water in tanks can be monitored to check that the temperature/pH/oxygen level is OK. / It's easier to control how much food is supplied and give exactly the right sort of food. / The water can be removed and filtered to get rid of waste food and fish faeces. / There's no interspecific predation indoors. *[1 mark for each]*

b) E.g. select the fish with the biggest muscle mass and breed them together *[1 mark]*. Select the best of the offspring/the offspring with the biggest muscle mass and breed them together *[1 mark]*. Repeat over several generations to produce fish with a high protein yield *[1 mark]*.

It's the muscles of the fish that provide us with protein, so you need fish with a high muscle mass to produce a high protein yield.

Mixed Questions for Paper 1

Pages 47-48 — Mixed Questions for Paper 1

1 a) i) Neutrophils/phagocytes ingest pathogens *[1 mark]*. Therefore a reduction in the number of neutrophils/phagocytes means that invading pathogens are less likely to be destroyed, leading to a higher risk of infection *[1 mark]*.

   ii) mild neutropenia *[1 mark]*

1.2×10^6 / cm^3 is 1 200 000 / cm^3. The ranges for the ANC in the table are given per mm^3, so you need to work out the count per mm^3 to answer the question. A mm^3 is 1000 times smaller than a cm^3, so 1 200 000 ÷ 1000 is 1200 / mm^3, which falls in the range of values given for mild neutropenia.

   b) E.g. if food cannot be digested properly, vitamins and minerals/vitamin D and calcium may not be absorbed *[1 mark]*. Some vitamins and minerals/vitamin D and calcium are needed to make bones and teeth *[1 mark]*.

2 a) D *[1 mark]*

Secondary consumers eat primary consumers — so in this food web, the Indian toad, wild boar, giant squirrel, eagle and Asiatic lion are secondary consumers.

   b) When the deer sees the lion its adrenal glands release adrenaline into the blood *[1 mark]*. Adrenaline binds to receptors in the deer's heart *[1 mark]*, causing the cardiac muscle to contract more frequently, increasing the deer's heart rate *[1 mark]*. When the deer runs away, its muscles need more energy, so it respires more, causing the amount of carbon dioxide in the blood to increase *[1 mark]*. This is detected by receptors in the aorta/carotid artery, which sends impulses to the deer's brain *[1 mark]*. The brain then sends impulses to the heart, causing it to contract more frequently, increasing heart rate further *[1 mark]*.

   c) There need to be more chital deer to support all of the lions, because not all of the energy from the deer is passed on to the lions *[1 mark]*. This is because the lions don't eat all of the chital deer (e.g. bones) *[1 mark]*. Also, not all of the material that the lion eats is digestible, so some passes through the lion and comes out as waste, e.g. faeces *[1 mark]*. Some of the material that is taken in is used for respiration and is eventually transferred to the surroundings by heat *[1 mark]*.

   d) E.g. the scientist could have divided the area into a grid and then randomly selected a set number of coordinates (e.g. by using a random number generator) *[1 mark]*. She could have placed quadrats down at each of these coordinates and counted the number of *Chloris barbata* in each quadrat *[1 mark]*. She could have then calculated the mean number per quadrat and used this value to calculate the mean number of *Chloris barbata* per m² *[1 mark]*. The scientist could have then multiplied this value by the total area studied to give an estimate of the population size *[1 mark]*.

Pages 49-50 — More Mixed Questions for Paper 1

1 a) E.g. ancestors of the hare population will have shown variation in their ear size *[1 mark]*. Hares with smaller ears are more suited to a cold environment because they will lose less heat, so small-eared hares in the population would have been more likely to survive in the cold *[1 mark]*. These hares will have been more likely to successfully reproduce *[1 mark]* and pass on the alleles that give rise to small ears to the next generation *[1 mark]*. Over time the alleles for smaller ears will become more common in the population and eventually all the hares will have small ears *[1 mark]*.

   b) E.g. vasodilation may occur in the blood vessels that supply the capillaries near the surface of the ears *[1 mark]*. This will increase blood flow to the ears, allowing more energy to be transferred to the surroundings, cooling the hare down *[1 mark]*.

   c) Curling up reduces the hares' total surface area *[1 mark]*, meaning that they lose heat more slowly as there is less area for energy to transfer across *[1 mark]*.

2 a) E.g. villi provide a large surface area for the exchange of substances by diffusion *[1 mark]*. / Blood from the fetus and from the mother run in close contact to one another, reducing the distance substances need to diffuse *[1 mark]*.

   b) 39 dm³ = 39 000 cm³
   39 000 ÷ 60 = 650
   650 ÷ 60 = 10.83... = **11 cm³ per second** (to 2 s.f.)
   [2 marks for a correct answer, otherwise 1 mark for correct working]

   c) i) E.g. the fetus may not receive enough food/oxygen from the mother's blood to develop properly *[1 mark]*.

   ii) Vasodilation of the vessels supplying the placenta will increase the blood flow to the placenta from the mother (increasing the delivery of food and oxygen to the fetus) *[1 mark]*.

Mixed Questions for Paper 2

Pages 51-52 — Mixed Questions for Paper 2

1 a) The lack of root hairs means the roots don't have as much surface area for absorbing water from the soil *[1 mark]*. Therefore a higher concentration gradient of water between the soil and the root cells is needed to keep osmosis happening at a high enough rate *[1 mark]*.

b) E.g. carbon dioxide is a greenhouse gas and increased levels of greenhouse gases in the atmosphere cause global warming *[1 mark]*. Redwood forests absorbing large amounts of carbon dioxide helps to restore the balance of atmospheric gases disturbed by deforestation elsewhere / helps to counteract the carbon dioxide released by deforestation elsewhere *[1 mark]*.

c) E.g. a mutation will result in a change to the DNA sequence / a different mRNA codon being produced *[1 mark]*, which could change the amino acid sequence of the enzyme required for chlorophyll production *[1 mark]*. This could prevent the enzyme from being produced / change the shape of the enzyme's active site, so chlorophyll is not made *[1 mark]*.

d) E.g. they produce auxin *[1 mark]*, which accumulates on the shaded side of the stem *[1 mark]*. This causes the cells on the shaded side to elongate faster, which causes the stem to grow/bend towards the light *[1 mark]*.

e) i) E.g. the stomata in albino redwoods cannot close, meaning that they constantly lose water to the atmosphere through transpiration *[1 mark]*. This means that there's a continuous transpiration stream pulling ions up from the soil/roots to the needles, where the ions accumulate *[1 mark]*.

ii) E.g. the absorption of nickel ions from the soil by the albino growths means that the ions are absorbed in lower amounts by the parent plant, which is therefore not poisoned *[1 mark]*.

f) E.g. once the albino redwoods have been removed from the agar growth medium/planted into soil, they would have no way of obtaining nutrients on their own *[1 mark]* and so would not survive to develop/grow into full trees *[1 mark]*.

Pages 53-55 — More Mixed Questions for Paper 2

1 a) Any two from: e.g. thylacines suffered from introduced diseases. / Dingoes out-competed thylacines for food. / Dingoes out-competed thylacines for territory. *[2 marks]*

b) 1803 to 1936 = 133 years
3000 thylacines ÷ 133 years = **23.6 thylacines per year**
[2 marks for correct answer, otherwise 1 mark for correct working]

c) E.g. a nucleus could be extracted from a body cell of preserved biological material from a thylacine *[1 mark]*. The nucleus could be removed from the egg cell of a related species/a Tasmanian devil *[1 mark]*. The nucleus of the thylacine could then be inserted into this enucleate egg cell/this egg cell with its nucleus removed *[1 mark]*. An electric shock could be used to stimulate the egg cell to divide to form an embryo *[1 mark]*. Once the embryo had developed into a ball of cells it could be implanted into the uterus of an adult female of a related species/Tasmanian devil *[1 mark]* to continue to grow into a genetically identical copy (clone) of the preserved thylacine *[1 mark]*.

2 a) E.g. mineral fertilisers contain nitrates/phosphates *[1 mark]*. If too much fertiliser is applied to the fields, it will run off the fields when it rains into nearby water sources, leading to eutrophication *[1 mark]*. This is where excess nitrates/phosphates/nutrients in the water cause algae to grow fast and block out light *[1 mark]*. This means that less light reaches plants, which then can't photosynthesise and so die *[1 mark]*. The microorganisms that feed on dead plants increase in number and use up the oxygen in the water *[1 mark]*. This means that there is not enough oxygen available for other organisms, e.g. fish, which then also die *[1 mark]*. The death of all of these organisms reduces biodiversity *[1 mark]*. *[Maximum 6 marks available]*

b) E.g. the food given to the fish/the waste produced by the fish leaks out into the surrounding water and increases the nutrient content of the water *[1 mark]*. This leads to eutrophication in the same way fertilisers in the water do *[1 mark]*.

c) E.g. sulfur dioxide causes acid rain *[1 mark]*. Acid rain may reduce biodiversity by changing the acidity of lake water so that plants and animals living in lake ecosystems die / by killing trees *[1 mark]*.

Biodiversity is the variety of living organisms. Anything that leads to the death of organisms will reduce biodiversity.

3 a)   Restriction enzymes may be used to cut out the insulin
       gene from the human genome and cut open a bacterial
       plasmid/vector *[1 mark]*. The gene and bacterial
       plasmid/vector may then be joined together with ligase
       enzymes *[1 mark]*. The plasmid/vector/recombinant
       DNA would then be inserted into a bacterial cell
       [1 mark]. The bacterial cell would then reproduce, until
       a population of bacteria that secrete human insulin was
       produced *[1 mark]*.

b) i) pituitary gland *[1 mark]*

   ii) E.g. the woman's eggs may not mature in the ovaries
       [1 mark]. This may prevent ovulation/the release of an
       egg *[1 mark]*.

  iii) E.g. because it may prevent/reduce sperm production
       [1 mark].

4 a)   E.g. by preventing chromosomes from separating /
       the nucleus from dividing *[1 mark]*.

b)   Plants treated with dinitroanilines would still have
       specialised cells *[1 mark]*, meaning that they may still
       be able to perform some specific functions essential for
       survival *[1 mark]*. However, the cells of plants treated
       with bipyridiliums are unlikely to be able to function
       at all *[1 mark]*, as without a cell membrane they would
       die/fall apart *[1 mark]*.

*Remember, one of the main functions of a cell membrane is to hold
the cell together.*